ENCYCLOPÆDIA
Britannica®
kids

BRAIN GAMES®

Power up your
BRAIN!

pi
kids®

phoenix international publications, inc.

Puzzle Constructors: Cihan Altay, Keith Burns, Myles Callum, Philip Carter, Clarity Media, Jeff Cockrell, Julie Cohen, Conceptis Puzzles, Melissa Conner, Don Cook, Jeanette Dall, Mark Danna, Harvey Estes, Adrian Fisher, Holli Fort, The Grabarchuk Family, Shelly Hazard, David Helton, Helene Hovanec, Robin Humer, Steve Karp, Allison Lassieur, Catherine Leary, Naomi Lipsky, Patrick Merrell, David Millar, Michael Moreci, Alan Olschwang, Ellen F. Pill, Fred Pisop, Planet X Graphics, Emily Rice, Stephen Ryder, Pete Sarjeant, Andrew Scordellis, Paul Seaburn, Lauren Anne Sharp, Vicky Shiotsu, Fraser Simpson, Howard Tomlinson, Wayne Robert Williams, Alex Willmore

Illustrators: Bryan Babiarz, Erin Burke, Giuseppe Conserti, Lisa Covington, Elizabeth Gerber, Alysen Hiller, Robin Humer, Sari Rantanen, Dave Roberts, Marilyn Roberts, Jay Soto, Shavan R. Spears, Jen Torche

Contributing Writers: Holli Fort, Kaara Kallen

Image Credits: Thinkstock; DesignWolf—iStock (girl: cover; boy: cover); Helen_Field—iStock (monitor: p. 110, p. 149; phone: p. 149, p. 159; school bus: p. 150, p. 155; paper: p. 163; shoes: p. 166); Annasunny—iStock (children: p. 110-111, p. 114, p. 133, p. 146, p. 151, p. 157, p. 159, p. 163, p. 166, p. 169; woman: p. 160); Dynamic Graphics—liquidlibrary (signs: p. 142, p. 168); VladislavMakarov—iStock (tools: p. 148); Octopus182—iStock (sander: p. 148); Olga_Aleksieieva—iStock (car: p. 150; plane: p. 154, p. 163, p. 174; dump truck: p. 155; scooter: p. 162; boat: p. 164, p. 171)

Published by Phoenix International Publications, Inc.

8501 West Higgins Road, Suite 300, Chicago, Illinois 60631
Lower Ground Floor, 59 Gloucester Place, London W1U 8JJ

www.pikidsmedia.com

p i kids is a trademark of Phoenix International Publications, Inc., and is registered in the United States.

ISBN: 978-1-5037-1466-3

Manufactured in China.

8 7 6 5 4 3 2 1

CONTENTS

Welcome to Britannica Kids Brain Games®!
This book is stuffed with all types of teasers to keep
your brain entertained: word puzzles, number codes,
mazes, visual challenges, and more! The book is
divided into five themes. In each, you'll find puzzles,
riddles, and fun facts related to the theme.

- All About Animals—feathery, furry,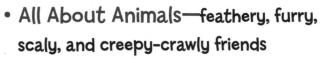
  scaly, and creepy-crawly friends

- From Farm to Fridge—food of all kinds and the places
  that produce food

- On Earth and Beyond—where we live, from our cities to our galaxy

- Art and Athletics— your favorite activities and pastimes

- Tech and Transport—things that go, and the engineering that drives them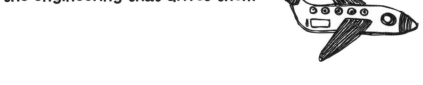

Did you know?

Solving puzzles is important work! During World War II, a team of code-
breakers in England headed by mathematician Alan Turing developed a machine
that could read encoded German messages. The machine solved a big puzzle
that helped the Allies win the war.

You can find all the answers at the end of the book—but give each teaser a good try before peeking! Here are some hints for working through the puzzles:

Do first things first

Make sure you read the directions so you know what you're getting into. For example, some puzzles can be solved in any order, but for others you have to start from a particular place and then build on the clues to work your way to the end. Pay attention to directions!

Change the pattern

If you get stuck, try thinking of the puzzle in a different way. For example, for jumbled-letter puzzles, try writing down the letters in a random pattern instead of a straight line. For a tricky maze, start a line from the FINISH as well as from the START, and see if you can get them to meet in the middle. These tricks may help you visualize possible connections in a different way and make the solution become clearer.

Use the right tool

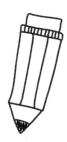

Everyone makes mistakes, and wrong turns can be part of the fun. A pencil with a good eraser will make it easier to take chances. For example, for "Picture This" jigsaws, if you find your lines don't quite connect from one square to the other, just erase and adjust!

Stop and rethink

If you get stuck on a puzzle, try these simple things to get unstuck:

- If the answers to a puzzle build on each other, step back and make sure that your answers to all the previous clues are correct. One wrong step along the way can cause problems later.

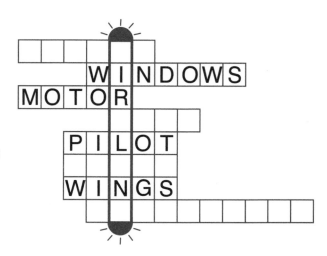

- If the puzzle doesn't have to be solved in order, go ahead and fill in the easiest answers first, then use those answers to help you figure out the harder ones.

- If you find you're not getting very far, switch to a different puzzle for a little while. When you return to the original puzzle, you may have a new perspective.

These pages are designed to keep you on your toes and, just as important, to be a lot of fun! Pick a puzzle and let's get started!

ALL ABOUT ANIMALS

Millions of different kinds of animals live on Earth. Animals are found throughout the world, from the freezing polar zones to the hottest deserts. They live on land and in the water. They come in a huge variety of shapes and sizes.

Like plants, animals need food and water to live. Unlike plants, which make their own food, animals feed themselves by eating plants or other animals. Animals can also sense what goes on around them. Their bodies allow them to move in reaction to their surroundings.

Find the Animal

Almost all of the letters in the alphabet are in this circle. But five of them are missing. Figure out which five letters aren't there, and write them on the blanks below. Unscramble the letters to reveal the hidden animal name.

___ ___ ___ ___ ___

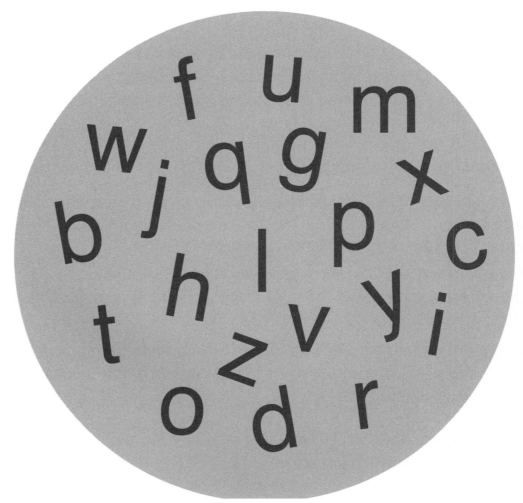

Answer on page 175

For the Birds

Place each bird word into the grid.

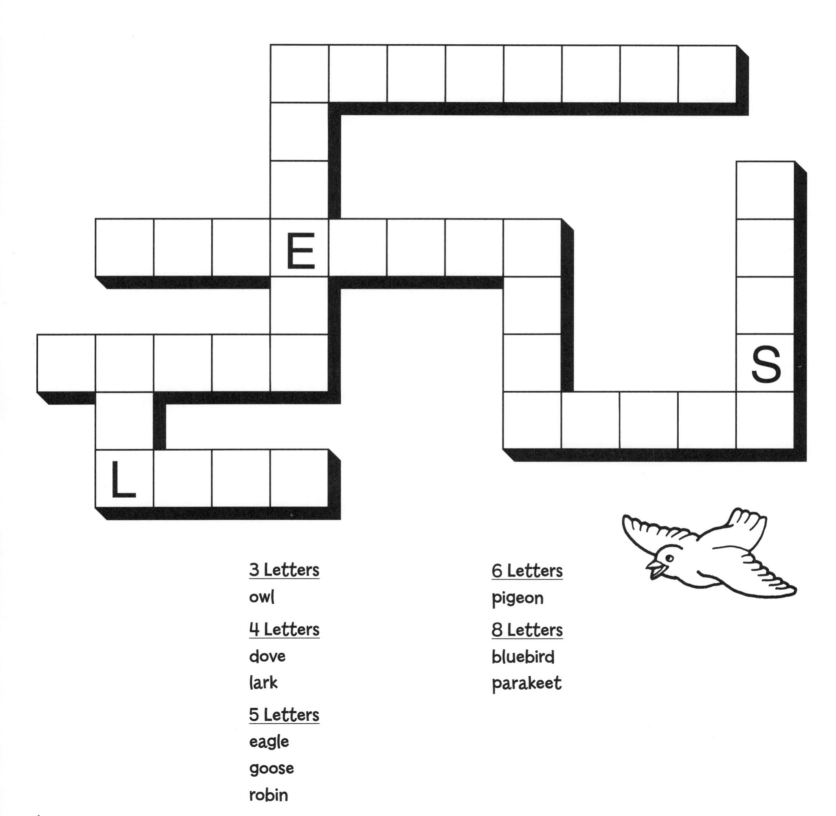

3 Letters

owl

4 Letters

dove

lark

5 Letters

eagle

goose

robin

6 Letters

pigeon

8 Letters

bluebird

parakeet

Tile Tie-Ins

Using the letter tiles below, complete the grid to reveal the names of 10 reptiles and amphibians.

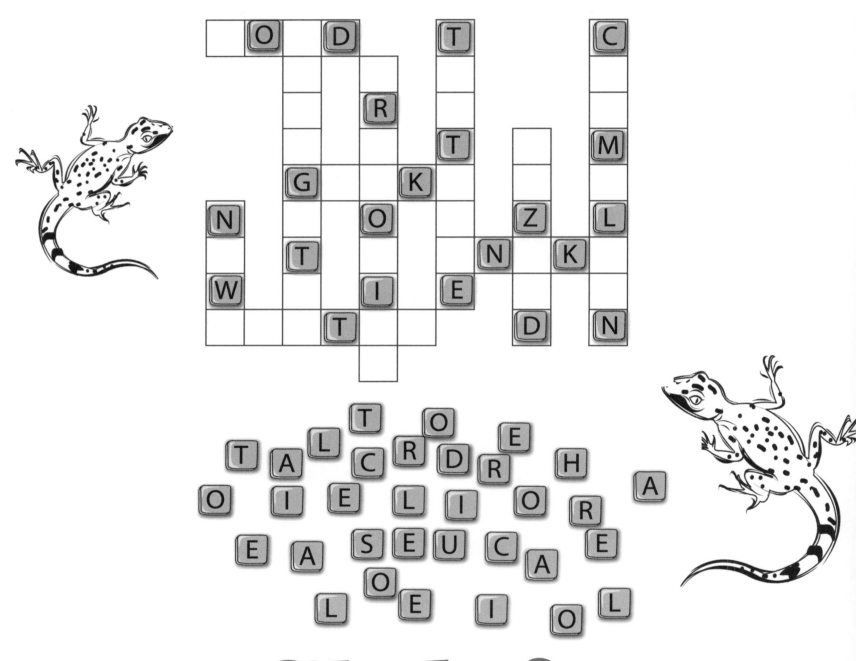

Did you know?

Some reptiles live longer than any other vertebrates. Certain turtles have lived for more than 100 years.

Answer on page 175

Bug Collection

There are a lot of bugs on display here. Which one bug appears most in this collection?

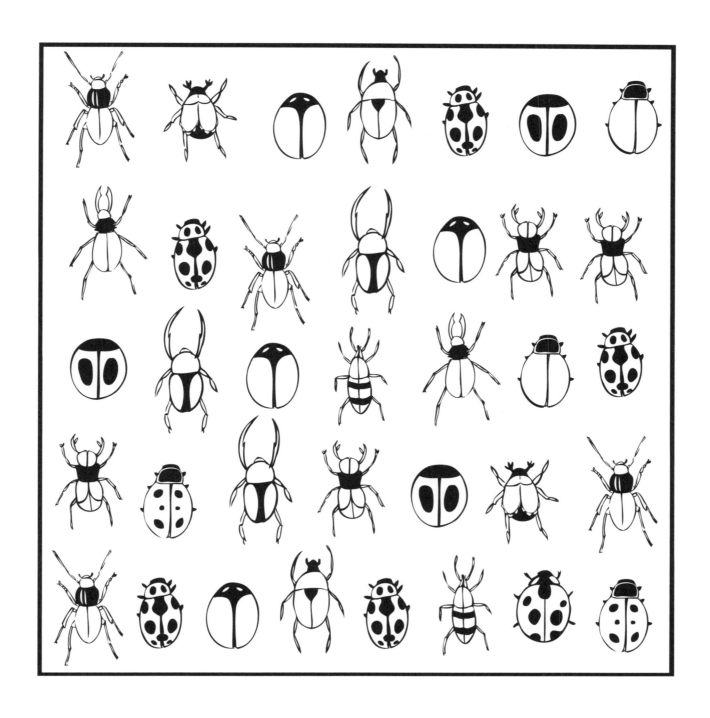

Picture-by-Number

Shade in the numbers that are divisible by two. Once complete, you will reveal a simple image.

39	63	53	85	20	80	10	36	33	27	33	61
25	81	51	76	91	21	29	3	34	25	11	49
15	80	54	51	43	19	43	29	71	92	20	17
38	27	25	73	68	91	93	44	95	7	59	78
58	15	94	65	59	56	66	45	75	66	25	4
56	7	39	83	79	29	63	77	87	67	49	32
75	56	42	51	17	30	4	15	83	16	78	17
73	17	45	52	5	51	11	89	46	21	69	39
17	33	51	97	86	51	43	96	47	25	51	31
15	55	77	58	3	87	91	71	34	49	69	7
91	45	72	95	7	85	17	9	21	90	57	73
51	51	60	1	2	41	33	98	9	60	91	27

Answer on page 175

Leapfrog

Grow from a tadpole to a hopping frog over the course of this maze.

FINISH

START

Did you know?

There are more frogs than any other kind of amphibian. Other amphibians include toads and salamanders.

Come Together

Place each of the tile sets into the empty spaces below to create 3 nine-letter earth creatures. Each tile set is used only once.

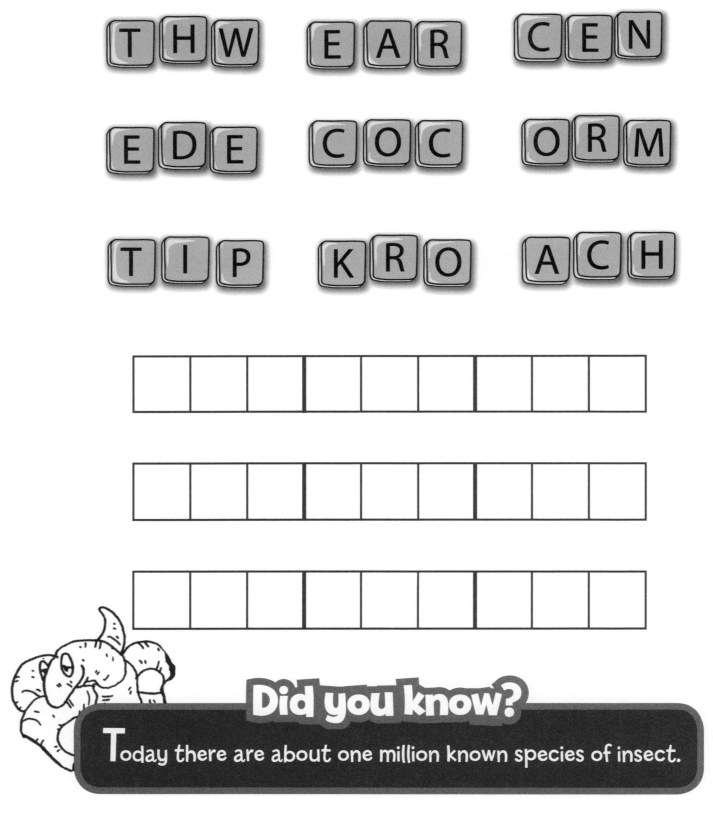

THW **EAR** **CEN**

EDE **COC** **ORM**

TIP **KRO** **ACH**

Did you know?

Today there are about one million known species of insect.

Answer on page 175

Add-a-Letter

Rearrange the tiles from each word, adding one new tile from the bottom in order to form the name of an animal in the empty boxes. Each tile from the bottom of the page is used only once.

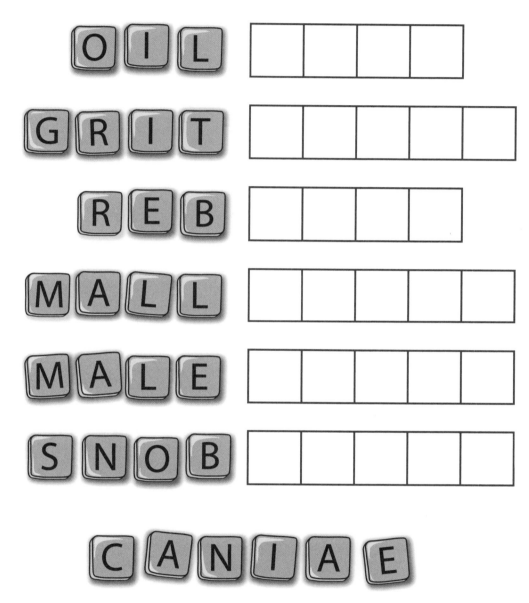

O I L

G R I T

R E B

M A L L

M A L E

S N O B

C A N I A E

13

Word Swatter

Use three letters from the words below to create six common words. Letters will be used more than once but will not repeat in each word.

Did you know?

Because it is sometimes mistaken for a swimming person, the sea cow, or manatee, may have given rise to the folklore of mermaids.

Answer on page 175

Bee Maze

Help the bee find its way to the flower at the center of the maze.

Tile Tie-Ins

Using the letter tiles below, complete the grid to reveal the names of 12 animals.

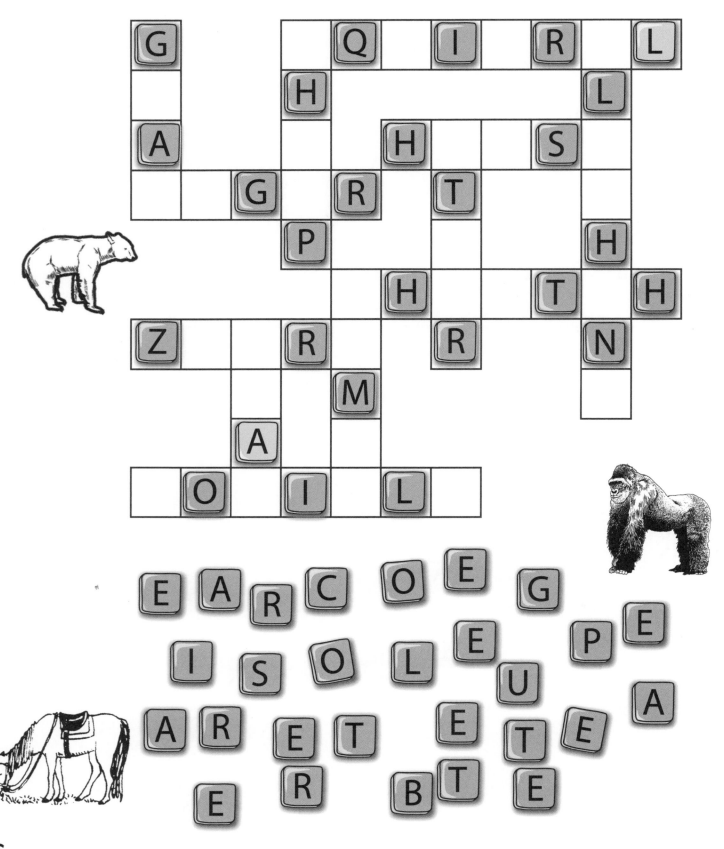

Answer on page 175

Riddle in the Middle

Use the clues to complete the five-letter answers, starting at the top and working your way down. When finished, read the letters in the squares with the thick boxes, from top to bottom, to reveal the answer to the riddle below.

Q: What do elephants have that no other animal has?

A: _ _ _ _ _   _ _ _ _ _ _ _ _ _ _ _ _ !

1. Product tag

   | L | | | | L |

2. Something to sit on

   | C | | | | R |

3. Waiting area

   | L | | | | Y |

4. Poetic match

   | R | | | | E |

5. Meat entrée

   | S | | | | K |

6. Postpone

   | D | | | | Y |

7. Dairy product

   | C | | | | M |

8. Unoccupied

   | E | | | | Y |

9. Sneeze sound

   | A | | | | O |

10. Courageous

    | B | | | | E |

11. Boxing blow

    | P | | | | H |

12. Stage performer

    | A | | | | R |

13. Untidy

    | M | | | | Y |

Did you know?

Elephants have good memories. They remember absent family members and places to find water.

Presto, Change-o!

You don't need a magic wand to change one animal into another! Make new words by changing just one letter in the name of each of these animals.

1. monkey _____

2. cat _____

3. dog _____

4. goose _____

5. mule _____

6. louse _____

7. jay _____

8. bear _____

9. loon _____

10. skink _____

18

Answer on page 176

Crustacean Crossing

Get this crab off the beach and back into the water.

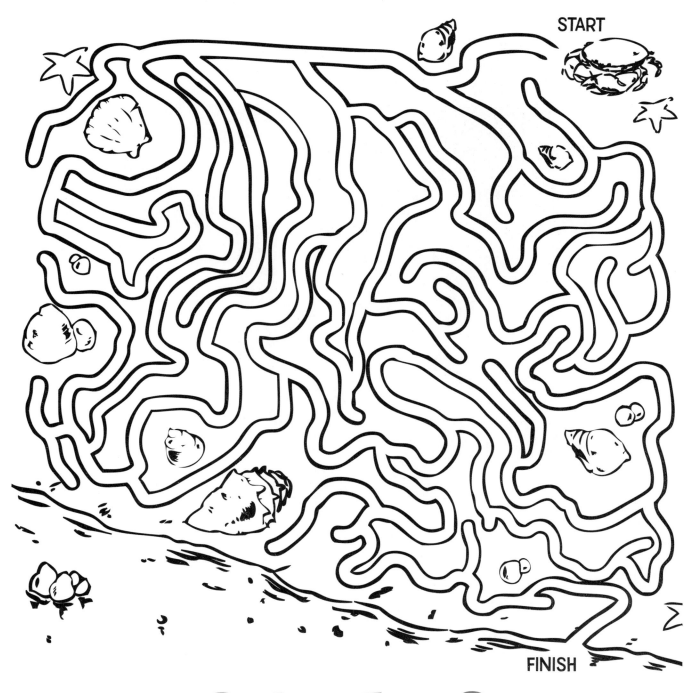

START

FINISH

Did you know?

Female blue crabs mate only once in their lives.

Find the Blocks

Find the shape at the right in the grid as many times as listed. The shapes must be facing the same direction as the example.

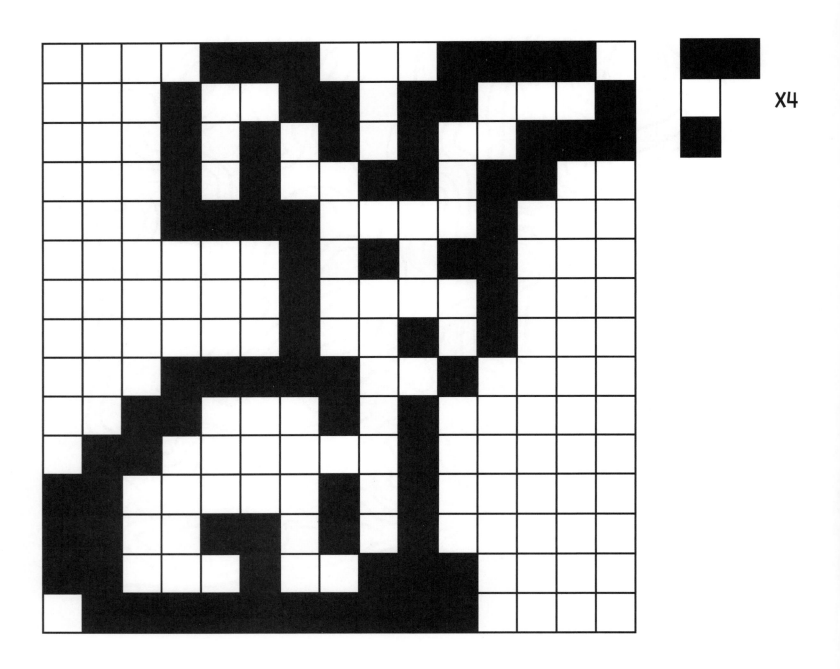

X4

Theme Park

This "ride" has a theme, but we can't tell you what it is. Place all the words in the boxes below—when you do, read the word created in the outlined boxes, from top to bottom, to reveal the theme.

ANTS   FLIES   BEETLES   GNATS   MOSQUITOES   ROACHES   WASPS

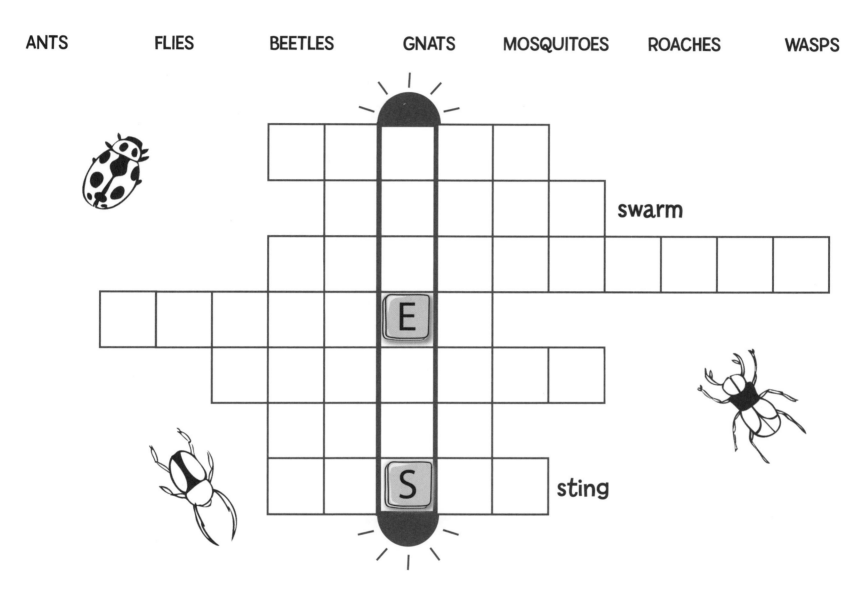

swarm

E

S

sting

Did you know?

Beetles have a variety of interesting defense mechanisms. For example, when threatened by a predator, bombardier beetles squirt an unpleasant-smelling, boiling-hot liquid from the rear of their abdomens with a loud popping sound. The noise and the liquid distract the predator, giving the beetle time to escape.

Bird Jumbles

Unscramble the letters to spell the names of eight kinds of birds. The boxed letters will give you the answer to this riddle:

Q: What happens to a duck when he flies upside down?

A: He __ __ __ __ __ __ __ __!

AIULQ

☐ __ __ I __

EKAETPAR

P __ __ __ ☐ __ E __

LSLEUAG

S __ __ __ __ ☐ __ L

RTISCHO

O ☐ __ R __ __ __

LGEAE

__ ☐ G __ __

CAUNOT

T __ ☐ __ __ N

WOCR

☐ __ __ __

NIUNEPG

☐ __ __ G __ __ N

Did you know?

Birds are more closely related to reptiles than they are to mammals. Many scientists think that birds developed from dinosaurs millions of years ago.

Answer on page 176

Reword Rewind

Unscramble the tiles to form words that will complete the sentence.

Our class won a ⬜⬜⬜⬜ trip to see the coral ⬜⬜⬜⬜ .

- -

A Trail of Threes

Help the tiger get back to the jungle. Make a path by drawing a line through the spaces that have multiples of three (such as 12 and 24).

(Hint: Here's a quick way to tell if a number is a multiple of three: The sum of its digits will be divisible by three!)

3	12	27	15	24		
4	2	10	7	11	8	6
13	16	48	39	9	30	21
20	23	33	26	14	5	29
45	36	42	32	90	93	18
60	37	40	46	69	61	99
66	54	63	72	96	70	

Pict-o-Matic

Whoops! Our picture got scrambled! To put it back together, copy each box into the empty grid (the letters and numbers tell you which box to fill in).

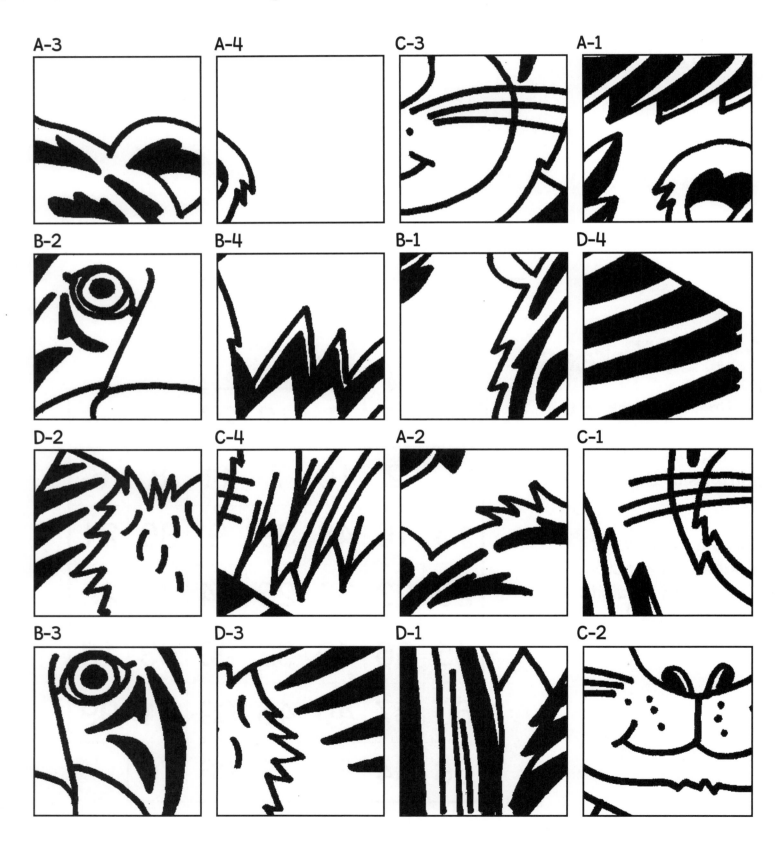

	1	2	3	4
A				
B				
C				
D				

Did you know?

Asia is the only continent where tigers are found in the wild.

Come Together

Place each of the tile sets into the empty spaces below to create 3 nine-letter birds. Each tile set is used only once.

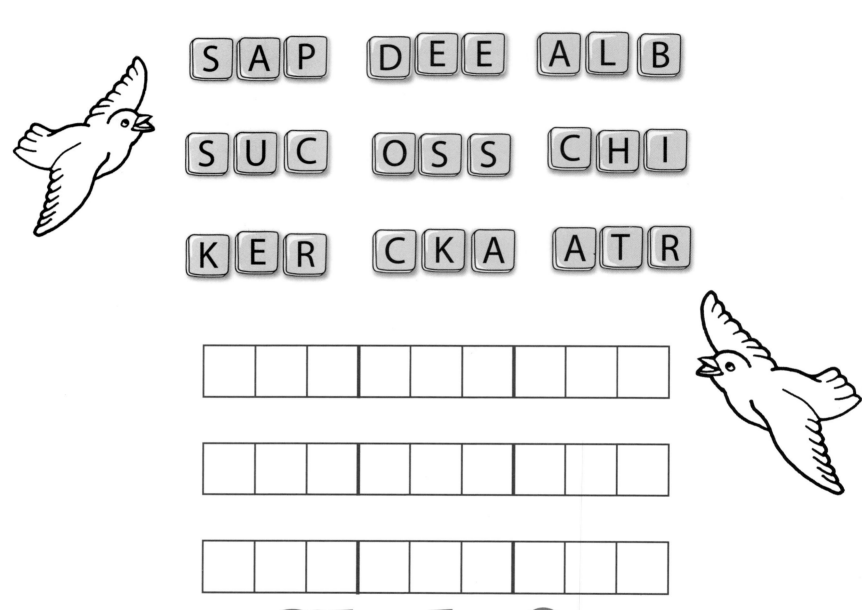

SAP DEE ALB

SUC OSS CHI

KER CKA ATR

Did you know?

Flying birds have special features that allow them to fly. Their powerful chest muscles help them flap their wings. Many of their bones are hollow, which keeps them light. Their bodies narrow toward the ends like jet airplanes. Air flows smoothly over their feathers while they fly.

Answer on page 176

Piles of Tiles

Place all the tiles into the grid so they spell a jungle of safari-themed words. The tiles are compiled in specific groups—those groups will appear together in across or down entries.

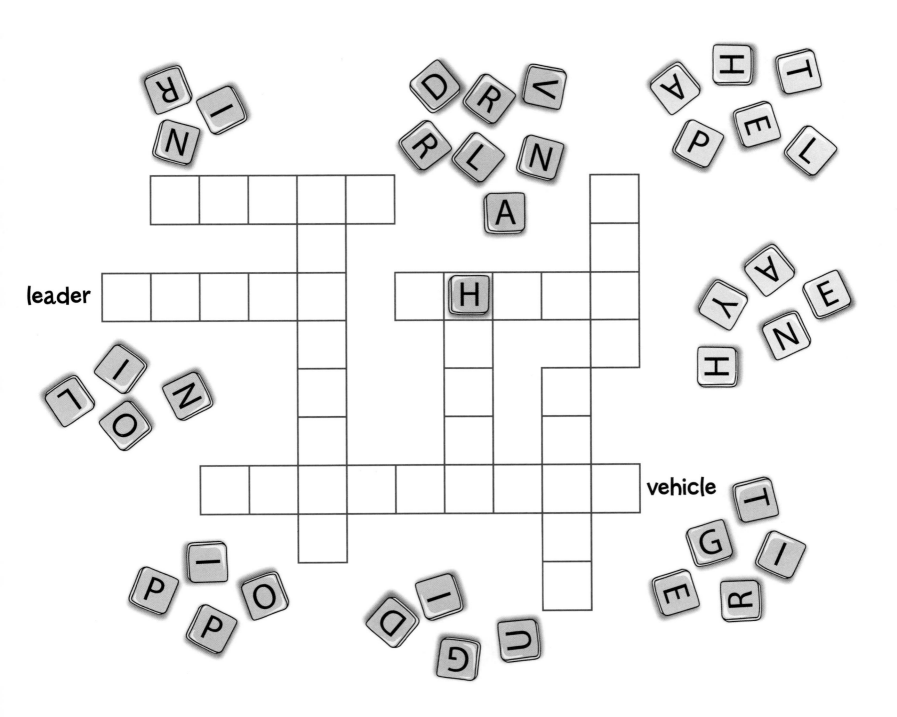

leader

vehicle

Find the Blocks

Find the shapes at the right in the grid as many times as listed. The shapes must be facing the same direction as the examples.

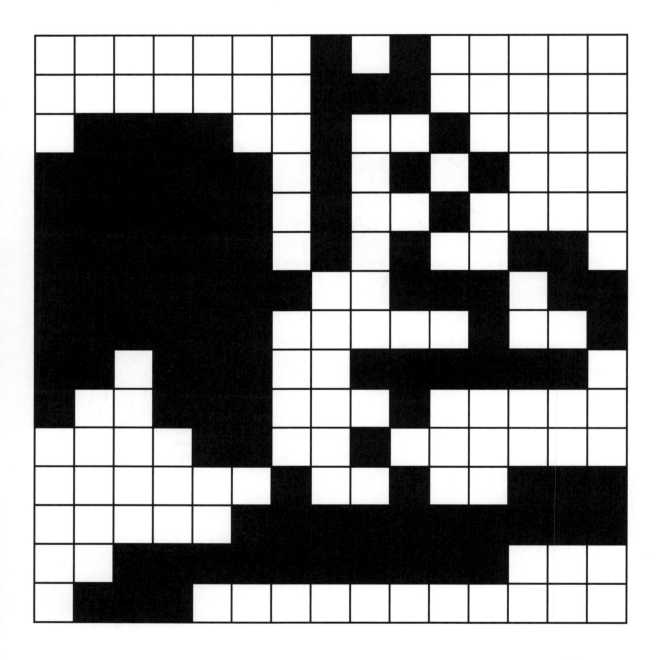

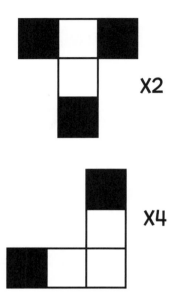

X2

X4

Did you know?

A squirrel's front teeth can grow six inches a year. Constant chewing keeps a squirrel's teeth short.

Answer on page 177

Honey Bear

Help the bear find a sweet reward at the end of the maze.

HONEY

Piles of Tiles

Place all the tiles into the grid so they spell different dangerous critters. The tiles are compiled in specific groups—those groups will appear together in across or down entries.

roars

stings

Answer on page 177

Find the Pair

Which two butterflies are identical?

A.

B.

C.

D.

E.

F.

Did you know?

Butterflies and moths have many features in common. One main difference is that most butterflies are active during the daytime. Moths generally are active at night.

Answer on page 177

Turtle Maze

Don't get lost as you navigate your way across the turtle's shell.

Start!

Finish!

Did you know?

The earliest fossils recognized as turtles are about 200 million years old—that's when dinosaurs roamed the Earth! Turtles have changed little in appearance since that time.

Answer on page 177

Theme Park

This "ride" has a theme, but we can't tell you what it is. Place all the words in the boxes below—when you do, read the word created in the outlined boxes, from top to bottom, to reveal the theme.

CLAM
GROUPER
JELLYFISH
OCTOPUS

PORPOISE
SHARK
SQUID
STINGRAY

SWORDFISH
TUNA
WHALE

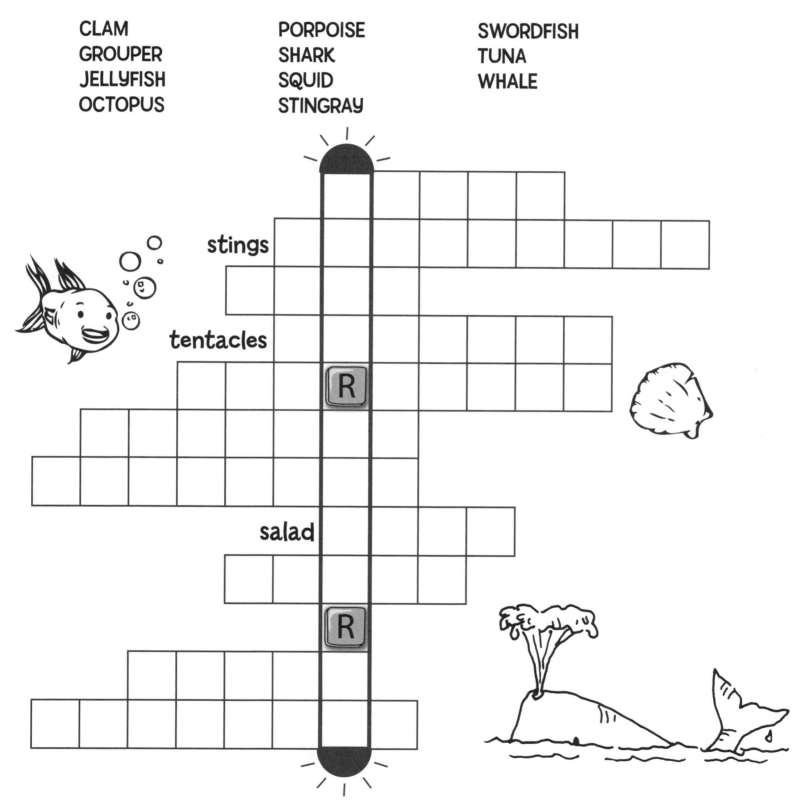

stings

tentacles

R

salad

R

The Ocean

Every word listed is contained within the group of letters below. Words can be found in a straight line diagonally, horizontally, or vertically. They may be read either forward or backward.

```
S O T E S E A H O R S E H E
T E C E E N T P Y H E K L I
I R D T E B O M S L C A E R
N E O A O A A I T N H N R E
G L L N I P F R E W B S A B
R C P A S L U H R A E A L M
A A H M E T F S F A A E L U
Y N I G A N A Q H E C S O C
V R N E C R O U T A H U D U
O A S E D D N I H C R U D C
H B B I Y A P D L E B K N A
C O N C H N I L R A M B A E
N E L E C T R I C E E L S S
A N E M O N E G N O P S L E
```

ANCHOVY	DOLPHIN	SARDINE	SHRIMP
ANEMONE	ELECTRIC EEL	SEA CUCUMBER	SPONGE
ANGELFISH	MANATEE	SEAHORSE	SQUID
BARNACLE	MARLIN	SEA LION	STINGRAY
BARRACUDA	OCTOPUS	SEA SNAKE	URCHIN
BEACH	OYSTER	SEA TURTLE	WHALE
CONCH	SAND DOLLAR	SHARK	

Answer on page 177

Picture This

Copy the picture in each numbered square into the same numbered square in the grid to reveal a gentle giant.

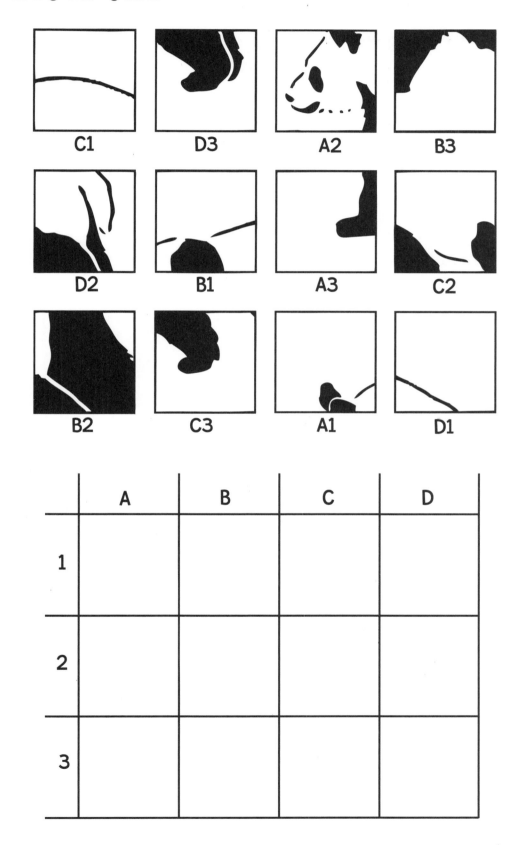

C1   D3   A2   B3

D2   B1   A3   C2

B2   C3   A1   D1

	A	B	C	D
1				
2				
3				

Did you know?

Giant pandas are found only in bamboo forests in central China. They can stand on their hind legs and do somersaults!

Insect Anagrams

Unscramble the letters to spell the names of eight common insects. Then read all the boxed letters in order to find out the answer to this riddle:

Q: Why wouldn't they let the butterfly into the dance?

A: It was a __ __ __ __ __   __ __ __ __ __!

SO TO QUIM

□__ __ __ __ __ __ __

ANGRY FOLD

__ __ __ __ __ □__ __ __ __

TRY ELF TUB

__ __ __ __ □__ __ __ __ __

GRAPH SPORES

__ __ __ __ __ __ □__ __ __ __ __

BALD GUY

__ __ __ __ □__ __ __

A RILL CARPET

__ □__ __ __ __ __ __ __ __ __

LET BEE

__ __ __ __ □__ __

FRY HOLES

__ __ __ __ __ __ □__ __

Answer on page 178

Spiderweb

A butterfly is tangled in a spider's web. Can you help her find the way out?

Did you know?

Spiders are the only animals that digest their food outside their bodies.

Bird Watching

How many birds are in this picture?

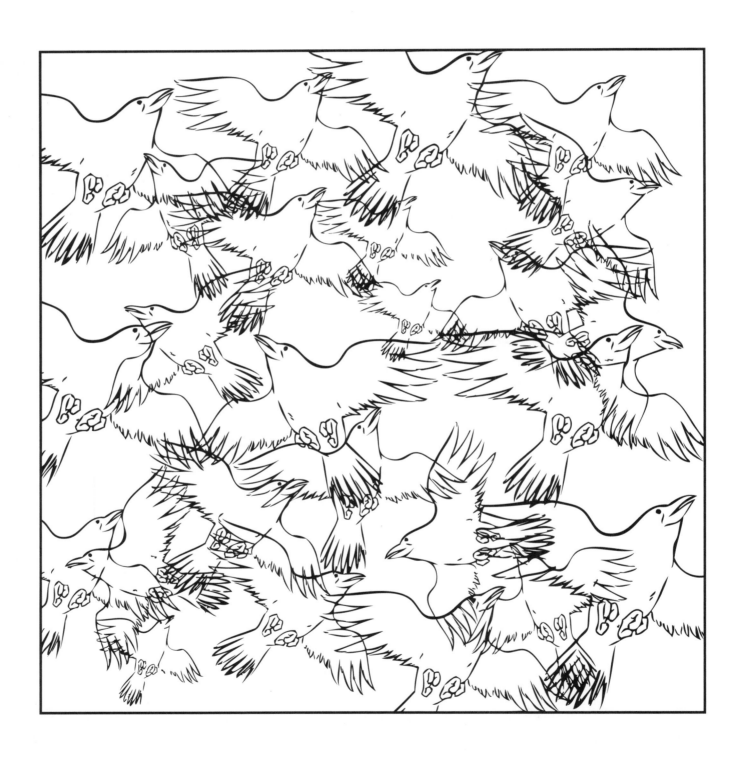

Answer on page 178

Picture-by-Number

Shade in the numbers that are divisible by 13. Once complete, you will reveal a simple image.

121	170	162	81	177	170	28	152	160	178	11	161	175	167	46
148	176	24	43	192	110	154	160	122	92	89	152	57	102	123
21	106	103	121	72	163	116	191	55	39	181	54	61	175	19
153	119	112	44	157	47	148	125	116	118	182	195	118	106	96
131	128	110	123	174	43	24	176	108	186	13	176	130	78	135
62	139	106	35	6	161	192	4	61	51	52	39	26	26	175
158	170	68	94	61	47	181	157	138	185	169	143	95	15	142
33	187	16	180	177	24	28	32	151	71	13	41	9	175	27
192	59	88	91	14	75	35	26	134	88	169	95	128	125	108
6	51	182	156	195	152	91	169	117	196	65	135	27	96	81
54	7	104	182	13	47	65	117	52	190	13	183	139	110	33
114	143	156	104	156	143	26	182	65	143	195	90	62	116	179
15	169	195	104	143	182	117	143	195	195	195	175	174	55	24
182	3	39	26	130	130	156	52	143	169	52	106	29	7	21
52	51	39	26	65	13	78	65	104	78	7	44	172	77	140
2	190	77	143	91	182	182	52	143	131	142	53	116	119	157
54	77	106	169	182	159	37	59	195	65	73	45	9	135	145
174	170	129	143	177	13	172	184	78	12	182	101	49	30	112
154	82	140	182	73	65	151	89	65	69	65	33	66	87	18
109	107	104	8	137	148	74	117	45	165	110	122	200	74	140

Did you know?

A camel can lose 25 to 30 percent of its body weight when it is dehydrated.

FROM FARM TO FRIDGE

Farming includes growing and harvesting crops and raising animals. Farming provides the food and many raw materials that humans need to survive.

Crops all over the world make it to our tables in much the same way. When crops are ready to be eaten (and sometimes before), they are harvested. The crops are then boxed to be sent to the market. Sometimes, this market is a small, local market where people from the area come to buy fresh food. Other times, the food is loaded onto large trucks and shipped to supermarkets far away.

Reword Rewind

Unscramble the tiles to form words that will complete the sentence.

The chef took a road trip to ☐☐☐☐☐

a bowl of soup from every US ☐☐☐☐☐ .

T T A E S

Answer on page 178

Add-a-Letter

Rearrange the tiles from each word, adding one new tile from the bottom in order to form a type of fruit in the empty boxes. Each tile from the bottom of the page is used only once.

R A P

P A L E

U P L

E L M

C H A P

M O A N

P A G E

P G I M R E E

Pizza Pie

Get that pizza in the oven as quick as you can!

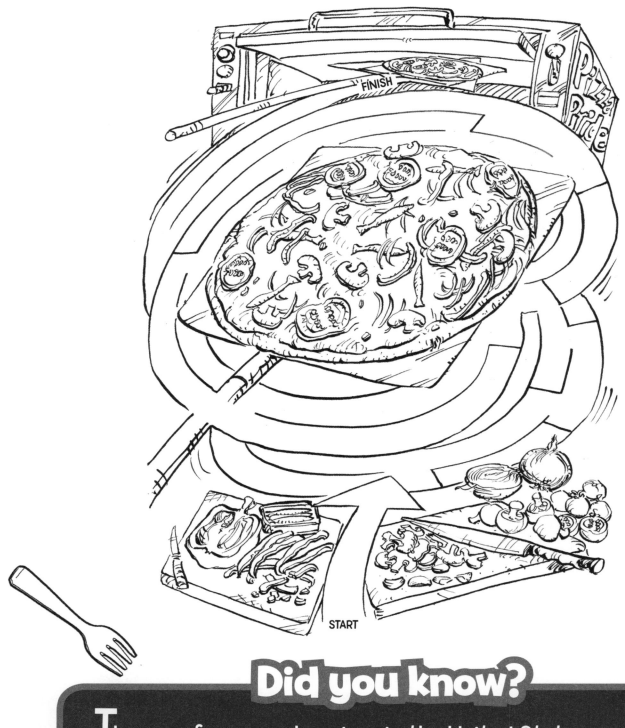

Did you know?

The use of oregano has risen in the United States mostly due to the popularity of pizza.

Answer on page 178

Out on the Farm

Can you spot the 10 differences between these two farm scenes?

Pic-doku

The grid below is divided into four sections. Your job is to have each of the four items appear in each section and in each row and column. Fill each square with the item's image or the letter that represents it. No item can repeat in any section, row, or column.

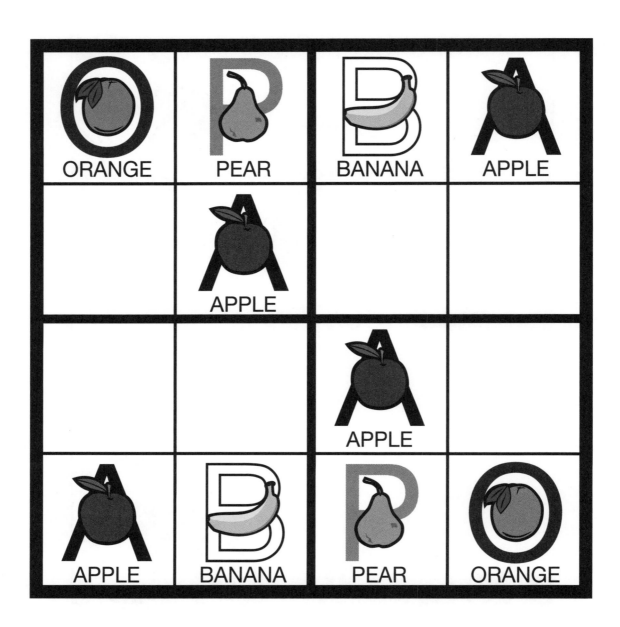

Did you know?

The first Sudoku world championship was held in March 2006 in Lucca, Italy.

Answer on page 178

Add-a-Letter

Rearrange the tiles from each word, adding one new tile from the bottom in order to form the name of a flower in the empty boxes. Each tile from the bottom of the page is used only once.

O R E

S I R

S A I D

C A L L

N O P E

R A T S

C H O I R

I Y Y D E S I

Road Block Flock

The road is blocked by sheep, and the delivery driver can't get through to make her delivery. Can you help guide her over the dirt track?

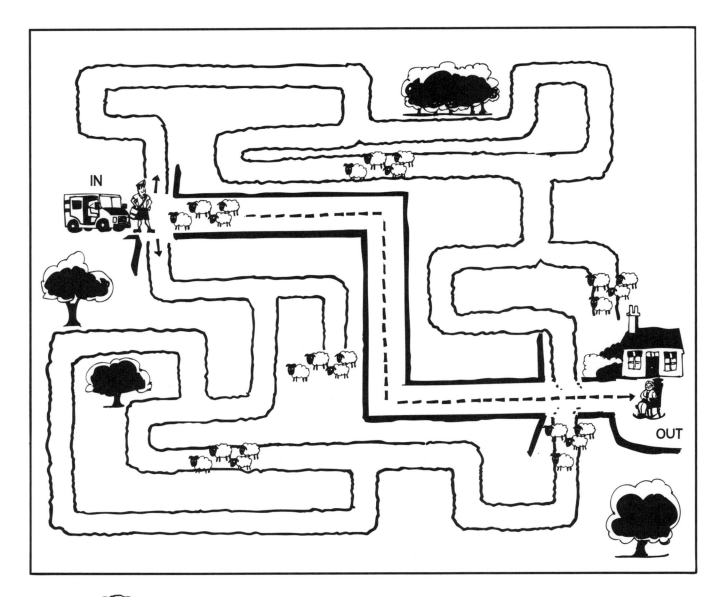

Did you know?

The Marco Polo sheep is named for the famous traveler who first described it. This type of sheep lives in Mongolia and is one of the largest in the sheep family.

Answer on page 179

Add-a-Letter

Rearrange the tiles from each word, adding one new tile from the bottom in order to form a vegetable in the empty boxes. Each tile from the bottom of the page is used only once.

S A N E

A P E

C H A I N S

B E S T

R O C

P R I N T S

N O O N S

I N S U P B E

Broken Egg #1

What number was painted on this egg before it was broken?

Did you know?

A 19th-century minister and humanitarian named Thomas Wentworth Higginson thought the bird's egg might be "the most perfect thing in the universe." Why do you think he said that?

Answer on page 179

Tile Tie-Ins

Using the letter tiles below, complete the grid to reveal 12 types of fruit.

A Calculated Joke

Solve the math problems, then put the corresponding letter underneath to spell out a riddle and its answer.

A	B	C	D	E	F	G	H	I	J	K	L	M	N	O	P	Q	R	S	T	U	V	W	X	Y	Z
19	45	32	43	26	9	11	23	30	48	37	4	33	29	20	7	44	31	25	40	3	16	15	18	47	38

Riddle:

$$\begin{array}{cccc} 30 & 16 & 20 & 10 \\ -15 & +7 & -1 & \times4 \end{array} \qquad \begin{array}{cc} 33 & 9 \\ +10 & +11 \end{array} \qquad \begin{array}{ccc} 38 & 40 & 22 \\ +9 & \div2 & -19 \end{array} \qquad \begin{array}{cccc} 8 & 21 & 20 & 2 \\ \times4 & -2 & \div5 & \times2 \end{array}$$

— — — —   — —   — — —   — — — —

— — — —   — —   — — —   — — — —

$$\begin{array}{ccc} 33 & 30 & 39 \\ +7 & \div2 & -19 \end{array} \qquad \begin{array}{cccccc} 9 & 23 & 31 & 14 & 39 & 11 & 5 \\ \times5 & -4 & -2 & +5 & -10 & +8 & \times5 \end{array}$$

— — —   — — — — — — —

— — —   — — — — — — —?

Answer:

$$\begin{array}{c} 15 \\ +4 \end{array} \qquad \begin{array}{cccc} 21 & 28 & 6 & 13 \\ \div3 & -9 & \times5 & +18 \end{array} \qquad \begin{array}{cc} 3 & 45 \\ +17 & \div5 \end{array}$$

—   — — — —   — —

—   — — — —   — —

$$\begin{array}{cccccccc} 32 & 4 & 35 & 19 & 35 & 33 & 23 & 21 \\ -7 & \div1 & -5 & -12 & \div5 & -7 & +8 & +4 \end{array}$$

— — — — — — — —

— — — — — — — —!

Did you know?

Although it is often called a tree, the banana plant is really a large herb.

Answer on page 179

Trotting Along

Start at the arrow and walk your horses down to the gate and back to where you started.

Picture Picnic

The eight objects below are hidden somewhere in the picture at the bottom of the page. Can you find and circle them all?

Did you know?

People are born with about 10,000 taste buds, but lose up to half of those cells as they age. This drop may explain why some foods, especially bitter foods, taste stronger to young people.

Answer on page 179

Reword Rewind

Unscramble the tiles to form words that will complete the sentence.

I went to the store and bought a ☐☐☐☐☐ for

the iced tea and a ☐☐☐☐☐ for the fruit salad.

Crossed Out

Use the given tiles to spell a pair of related words that meet on the given letter.

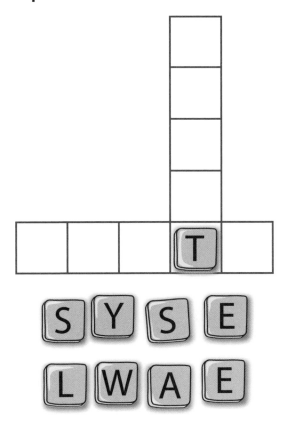

Tile Tie-Ins

Using the letter tiles below, complete the grid to reveal 10 types of seafood.

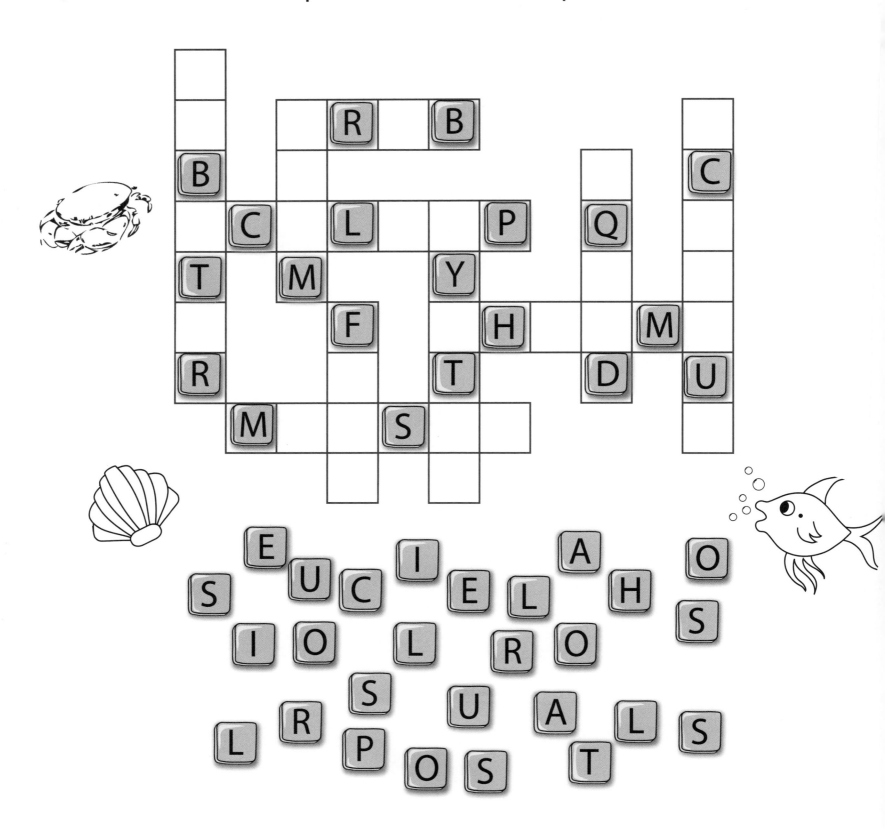

Answer on page 179

Number Code: Sounds Like Food

Solve each multiplication problem and write your answer on the first dash. Then, find the corresponding letter using the code on the right. Write the letter for that number on the second dash. Read down the column of letters to reveal words that sound like food.

CODE

❶ 5 × 2 = ___ ___
   2 × 6 = ___ ___
   5 × 5 = ___ ___
   9 × 2 = ___ ___

❹ 2 × 11 = ___ ___
   3 × 6 = ___ ___
   6 × 4 = ___ ___
   10 × 2 = ___ ___

❷ 3 × 5 = ___ ___
   4 × 6 = ___ ___
   2 × 12 = ___ ___
   4 × 4 = ___ ___

❺ 7 × 3 = ___ ___
   3 × 3 = ___ ___
   2 × 7 = ___ ___
   4 × 5 = ___ ___
   6 × 2 = ___ ___
   4 × 2 = ___ ___

❸ 3 × 7 = ___ ___
   2 × 8 = ___ ___
   4 × 3 = ___ ___
   13 × 2 = ___ ___
   3 × 8 = ___ ___

1. F	14. N
2. L	15. M
3. Z	16. T
4. C	17. G
5. J	18. R
6. H	19. V
7. O	20. D
8. Y	21. S
9. U	22. B
10. P	23. Q
11. W	24. E
12. A	25. I
13. X	26. K

Did you know?

The word "homophone" comes from Greek roots meaning "same sound." Homophones are words that sound alike but have different meanings.

Answer on page 180

Food Anagrams

Unscramble the capital letters to discover the names of five types of food. Read some of the ingredients for extra help!

1. MR BEAR HUG

lettuce

tomato

onions

—— —— —— —— —— —— —— —— ——

2. PAIL PEEP

apples

flour

sugar

cinnamon

—— —— —— —— —— —— —— ——

3. SIGHT TAPE

noodles

tomato sauce

meatballs

—— —— —— —— —— —— —— —— —— ——

4. MICE RACE

cones

sprinkles

hot fudge sauce

—— —— —— ——   —— —— —— —— ——

5. CHECKUP IS ON

carrots

celery

noodles

broth

—— —— —— —— —— —— —— —— ——

—— —— —— ——

Did you know?

In the Middle Ages, the King of France had his own personal anagram master.

Answer on page 180

Until the Cow Comes Home

Help the farmer bring this lost cow back to the barn.

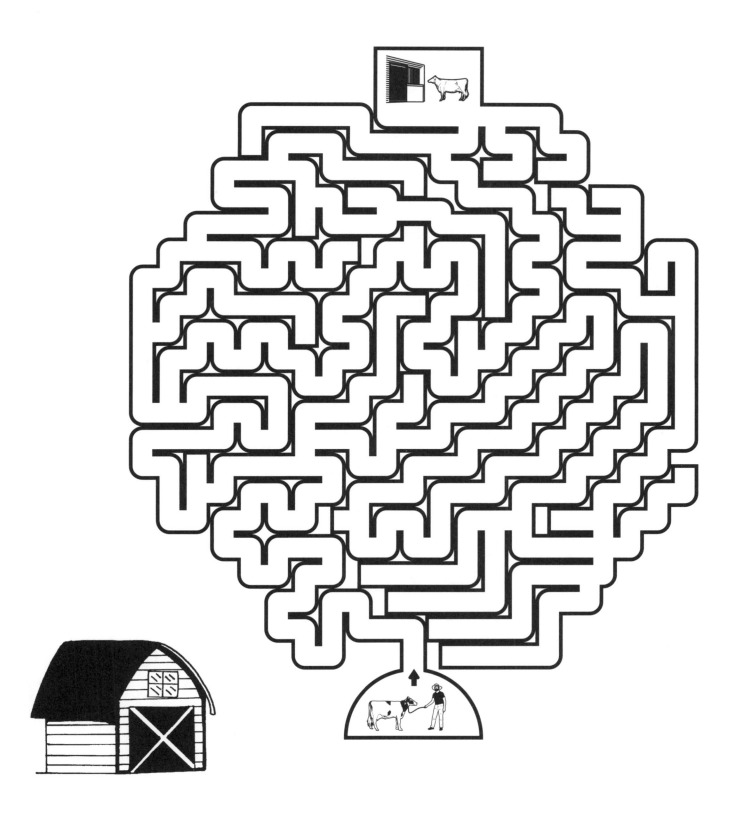

Farming

Every word listed is contained within the grid of letters below. Words can be found in a straight line horizontally, vertically, or diagonally. They may be read either forward or backward.

ACRE

CHICKEN

COMBINE

COWS

CROP

CULTIVATOR

DAIRY

EGGS

FEED

FERTILIZER

FLOCK

GANDER

GOOSE

GROW

INSECTICIDE

LAMB

LAND

MOWER

MULE

PASTURE

RANCH

REAP

SCARECROW

SEEDS

SHEEP

SHEPHERD

SILO

SOIL

TROUGH

```
N S C A R E C R O W L A M B V
J Y H E S O O G G U C G H F O
M I A E M M S I L O J O R E C
C J N B P U O X E A G A L R L
A C I S B H L W Z H N D E S R
H N F E E D E E E C X D D D E
E N N L A C T R H R N H A E Z
C H G U O R T L D A N V I E I
C N W P X C I I G K S L R S L
H V O S W E K O C E B U Y S I
I R R A H D R S I I T L Y G T
C E G U S E U C M S D C P G R
K L P W Y A E Y A F L E K E E
E P O I L L I P W W O R L P F
N C U L T I V A T O R E A P L
```

Answer on page 180

Number Code: Veggies

Solve each addition problem and write your answer on the first dash. Then, find the corresponding letter using the code on the right. Write the letter for that number on the second dash. Read down the column of letters to reveal the hidden words.

1
6 + 19 − 18 = ___ ___
13 + 13 − 2 = ___ ___
12 + 3 − 9 = ___ ___
6 + 9 − 4 = ___ ___

2
4 + 4 − 5 = ___ ___
14 + 4 − 12 = ___ ___
22 + 14 − 20 = ___ ___
2 + 27 − 13 = ___ ___
7 + 2 − 3 = ___ ___
5 + 12 − 15 = ___ ___
6 + 20 − 2 = ___ ___

3
4 + 5 − 6 = ___ ___
2 + 9 − 5 = ___ ___
4 + 13 − 9 = ___ ___
6 + 4 − 2 = ___ ___
4 + 8 − 11 = ___ ___
7 + 21 − 15 = ___ ___
9 + 14 − 12 = ___ ___

4
8 + 9 − 7 = ___ ___
7 + 23 − 6 = ___ ___
17 + 4 − 8 = ___ ___
26 + 2 − 15 = ___ ___
13 + 2 − 10 = ___ ___
2 + 9 − 8 = ___ ___
15 + 12 − 3 = ___ ___

5
30 + 5 − 11 = ___ ___
8 + 4 − 10 = ___ ___
23 + 9 − 30 = ___ ___
16 + 3 − 12 = ___ ___
17 + 5 − 12 = ___ ___
9 + 16 − 19 = ___ ___
6 + 7 − 9 = ___ ___
8 + 9 − 4 = ___ ___

CODE

1. O	14. H
2. G	15. V
3. C	16. B
4. N	17. W
5. U	18. X
6. A	19. Z
7. P	20. M
8. R	21. Y
9. D	22. Q
10. L	23. K
11. S	24. E
12. F	25. J
13. T	26. I

Did you know?

People first started cultivating vegetables sometime between 10,000 and 5,000 BCE.

Piles of Tiles

Place all the tiles into the grid so they spell types of sweet treats. The tiles are compiled in specific groups—those groups will appear together in across or down entries.

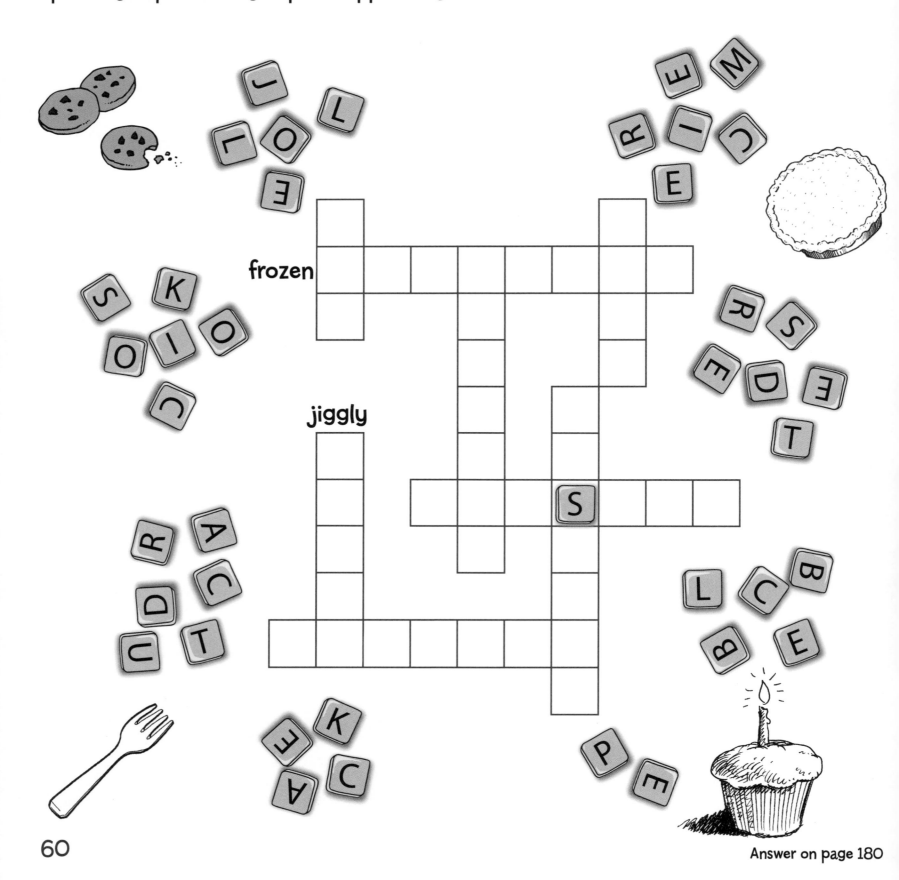

frozen

jiggly

Answer on page 180

Word Swatter

Use four letters from the word below to create 10 common words. Letters will be used more than once but will not repeat in each word.

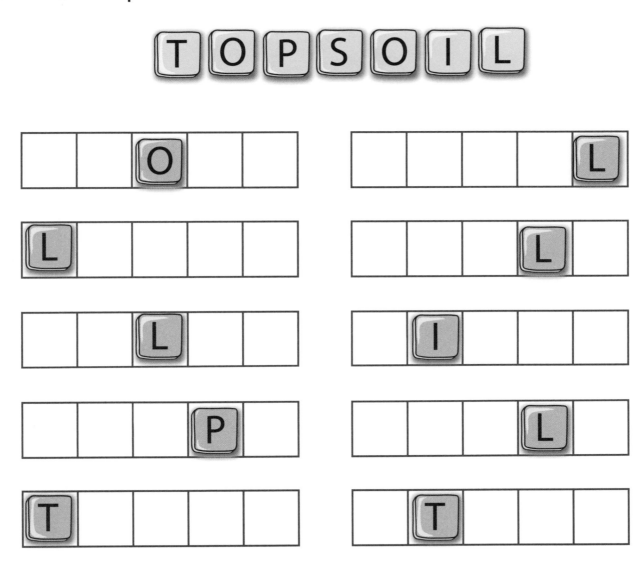

TOPSOIL

Did you know?

Nature takes 500 to 1,000 years to make one inch of the topsoil that plants need to grow! Preventing erosion and keeping farm soil healthy are important conservation steps.

Answer on page 180

Straw Vote

Which scarecrow is the mirror image of the one in the box?

A.

B.

C.

D.

E.

Answer on page 180

Tile Tie-Ins

Using the letter tiles below, complete the grid to reveal nine types of cooking herbs and spices.

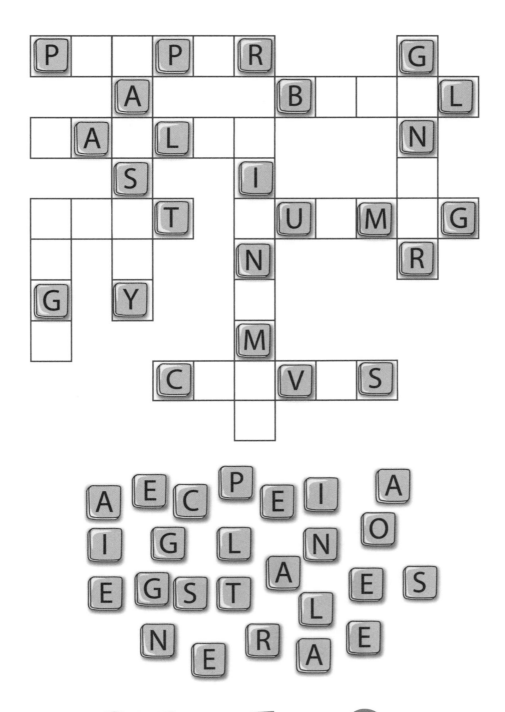

Did you know?

In ancient times, spices were used in medicine and to preserve foods.

Round 'em Up!

This cowboy has his work cut out for him! How many cows does he have to round up?

Did you know?

In India people let cattle roam freely throughout the cities and the countryside. This is because followers of Hinduism consider cattle to be holy.

Answer on page 180

Picture This

Copy the picture in each numbered square into the same numbered square in the grid, to reveal this trusty companion.

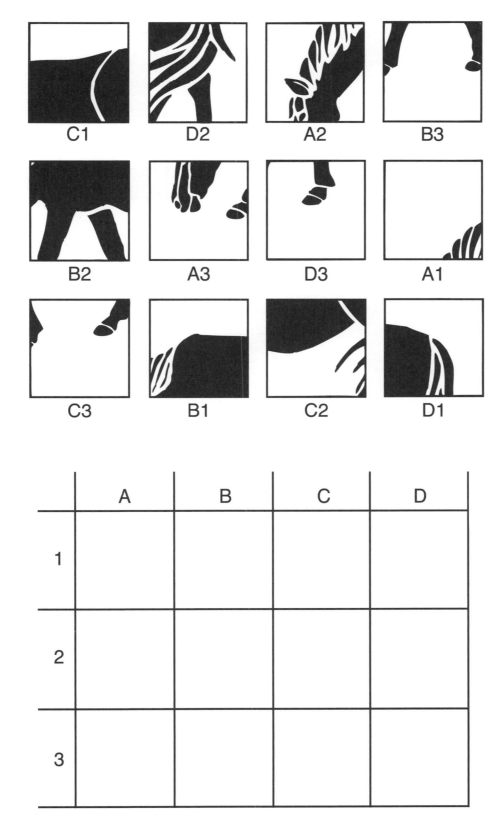

	A	B	C	D
1				
2				
3				

Answer on page 180

Add-a-Letter

Rearrange the tiles from each word, adding one new tile from the bottom in order to form a type of cheese in the empty boxes. Each tile from the bottom of the page is used only once.

CRIB

MARE

MAD

TAG

ATE

ARCHED

GOAD

UOEDFKC

Answer on page 181

Pic-doku

The grid below is divided into four sections. Your job is to have each of the four items appear in each section and in each row and column. Fill each square with the item's image or the letter that represents it. No item can repeat in any section, row, or column.

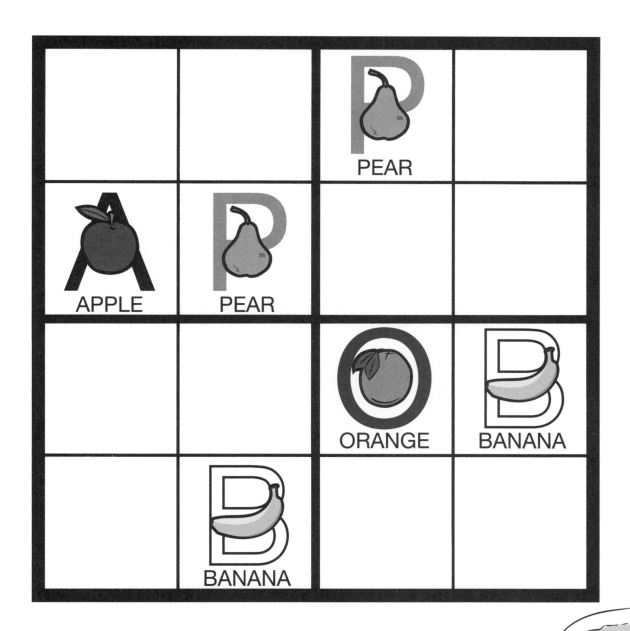

Find the Blocks

Find the shapes at the right in the grid as many times as listed. The shapes must be facing the same direction as the examples.

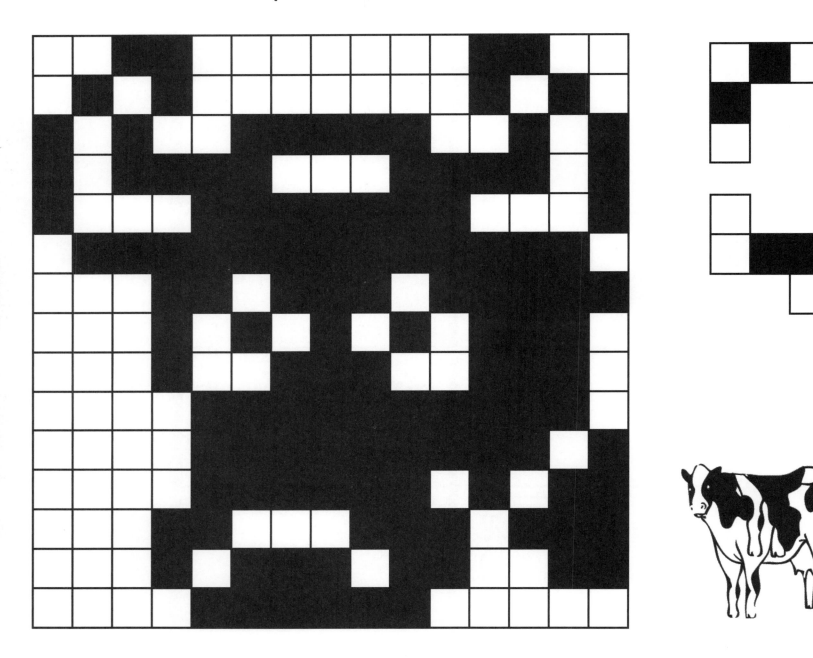

x1

x4

Did you know?

Cattle have no upper front teeth. When they graze, they grasp the grass with their mouth and swing their head to tear it from the ground.

Answer on page 181

Flower Power

Which floral design is the mirror image of the one in the box?

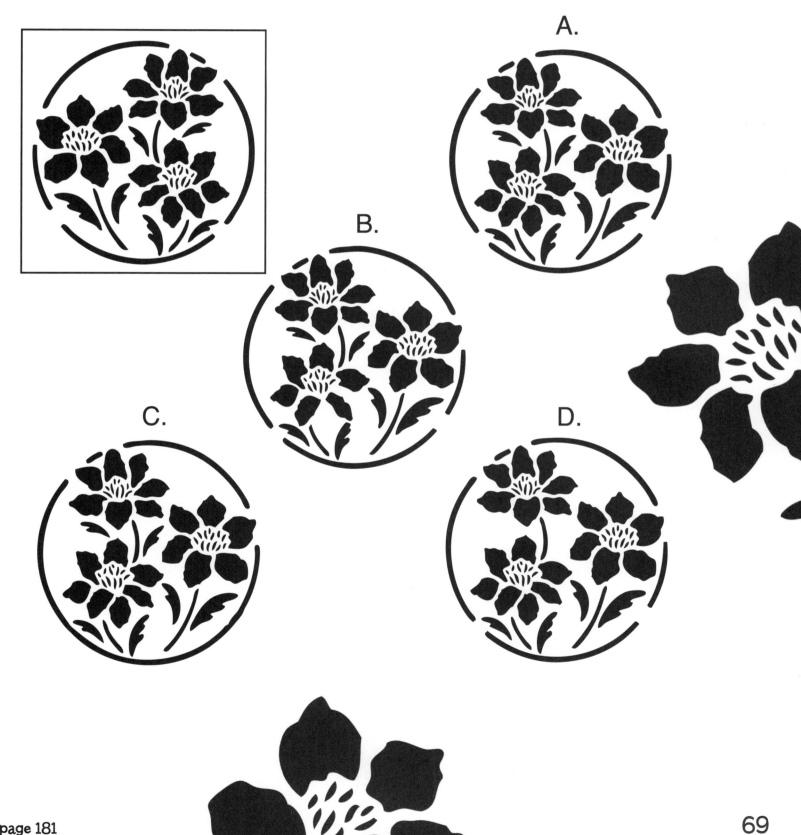

A.

B.

C.

D.

Fruits

Every word listed is contained within the group of letters below. Words can be found in a straight line diagonally, horizontally, or vertically. They may be read either forward or backward.

APPLE	KIWI
AVOCADO	KUMQUAT
BANANA	LEMON
BLUEBERRY	LIME
CATAWBA	LOGANBERRY
CHERRY	LOQUAT
COSTARD	MANGO
CRANBERRY	MEDLAR
CURRANT	MULBERRY
DAMSON	NECTARINE
DATE	OLIVE
DRUPE	ORANGE
DURIAN	PAPAYA

```
J Y N P P N B M D R A T S O C
R T Q M Q B A N A N A G L I O
P A P A Y A G Y E N L E W Y H
R U L B D R C R B Q G I F R A
U Q O L N K R J A N K O M R P
N M Q U I N C E A P D A T E P
E U U E R C I T B P E A R B L
E K A B A Y H S N N O T T N E
A N T E M E R E I H A N P A N
B N I R A P K R R A A G I R I
W H O R T L E B E R R Y O C R
A E C Y O G D R R B Y J A L A
T G Z A N T A U S A E O G V T
A N K A E L C M R I L S O N C
C A T I D P A I B I M C O L E
Y R R E B L U M V D A M S O N
P O M E L O E E C D E N O E G
D H M D R U P E O L S Q K N L
```

FIG	PEACH	PRUNE	TAMARIND
GOOSEBERRY	PEAR	QUINCE	TANGELO
GRAPE	PERSIMMON	RAISIN	TANGERINE
JAPONICA	POMELO	SLOE	WHORTLEBERRY

Answer on page 181

Leaping Labyrinth

Don't get too caught up in all the twists and turns as you negotiate your way to the center of this intricate sheep labyrinth.

FINISH

START

Did you know?

The hedge maze in the gardens at Hampton Court Palace was first planted during the reign of William III in the late 1600s.

Sixes and Sevens

Join together two letter groups from the box below to make a six- or seven-letter word that answers each clue. Write each word into the grid, going down. Be sure to match the number in the grid with the clue number. Cross off each letter group as you use it. When the grid is filled, read the circled letters from left to right to find the answer to this riddle:

Q: Why didn't the seafood salad get along with the rest of the meal?

A: ___ ___   ___ ___ ___   ___ ___ ___ ___ ___ ___!

Clues

1. Not public

2. Very smart

3. Speak in a very low voice

4. Breathe out

5. You drink beverages from these

6. "Lights, camera, ___ !"

7. The coldest part of a refrigerator

8. Duck sounds

9. Bed cover

10. Log homes

11. Major road for traveling

ACT	ALE	BLAN	BRI	CAB
CKS	EXH	FREE	GHT	GLAS
HIGH	INS	ION	KET	PER
PRI	QUA	SES	VATE	WAY
	WHIS	ZER		

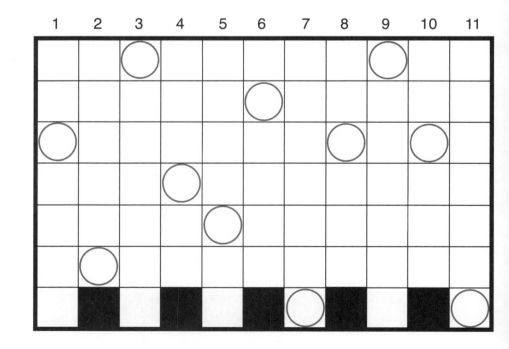

Answer on page 181

Broken Egg #2

What number was painted on this egg before it was broken?

Did you know?

The use of painted and decorated Easter eggs was first recorded in the 13th century. The church prohibited the eating of eggs during Holy Week. Since chickens continued to lay eggs during that week, these eggs became special.

Answer on page 181

ON EARTH AND BEYOND

Geography can be divided into two branches: physical geography and human geography. Physical geographers observe, measure, and describe Earth's surface. Human geography focuses on where people live, what they do, and how they use the land.

Astronomers study all of the objects outside Earth's atmosphere. These include the sun, moon, planets, stars, galaxies, and all other matter in the universe. Astronomy is one of the oldest sciences in the world.

Word Swatter

Use three letters from the words below to create 10 common words. Letters will be used more than once but will not repeat in each word.

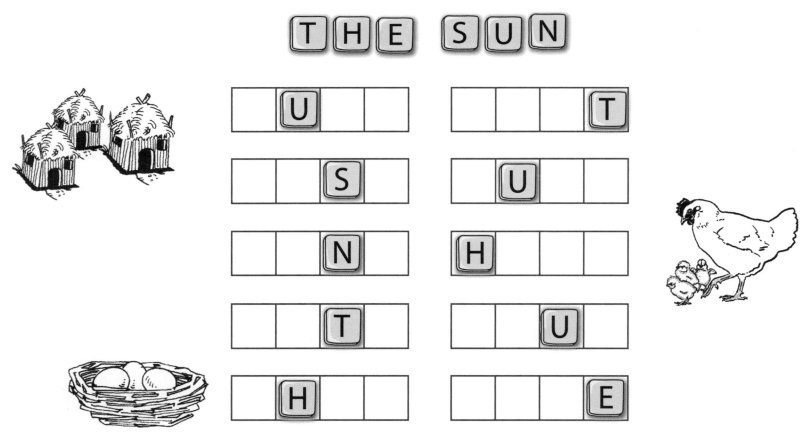

THE SUN

Answer on page 182

Piles of Tiles

Place all the tiles into the grid so they spell "spacey" words. The tiles are compiled in specific groups—those groups will appear together in across or down entries.

orbit

sun

Lost in Space

The astronaut wants to go home! Guide her through the maze and back to her spaceship.

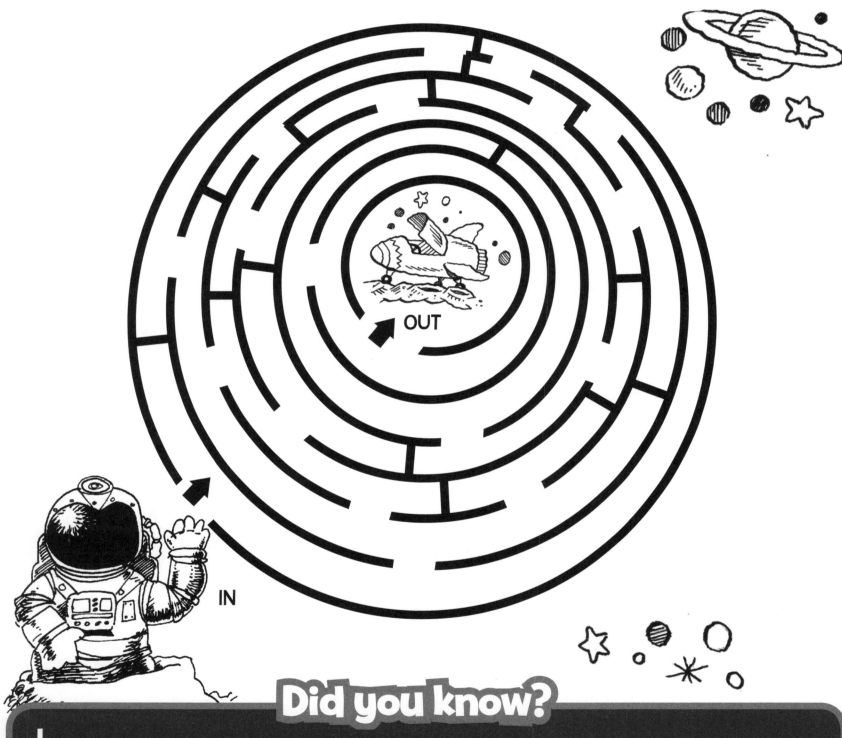

OUT

IN

Did you know?

In 1983 Sally Ride became the first American woman to travel into outer space. In 1984 Kathryn Sullivan became the first American woman to walk in space.

Answer on page 182

Sun's Out

Look in each box below. All the letters of the alphabet except one appear in each box. Find the missing letter and write it in the blank below each box for the answer. When you are finished, you'll have the answer to the following question:

Q: Our sun is actually one of these common heavenly bodies. What is it?

I	V	J	T	E
U	H	W	D	R
K	L	C	P	M
Y	B	O	G	Q
A	Z	N	X	F

_____

G	I	M	Q	F
L	A	X	C	N
P	V	W	Z	R
U	B	Y	D	J
E	K	S	O	H

_____

Q	R	U	V	E
Z	M	G	H	X
Y	B	N	F	P
C	T	I	O	W
S	D	J	K	L

_____

A	T	M	L	Q
F	O	W	X	I
V	N	C	G	Z
K	Y	D	H	B
E	S	U	P	J

_____

Come Together

Place each of the tile sets into the empty spaces below to create 3 nine-letter countries. Each tile set is used only once.

GUA GAP EZU

VEN ARA ORE

SIN NIC ELA

Did you know?

One of the answers is an island in Southeast Asia and is among the most densely populated countries in the world. Since the whole country is mostly one giant metropolis, it is considered a city-state.

Answer on page 182

Theme Park

This "ride" has a theme, but we can't tell you what it is. Place all the words in the boxes below—when you do, read the word created in the outlined boxes, from top to bottom, to reveal the theme.

CAMEL   DUNES   HEAT   LIZARD   OASIS

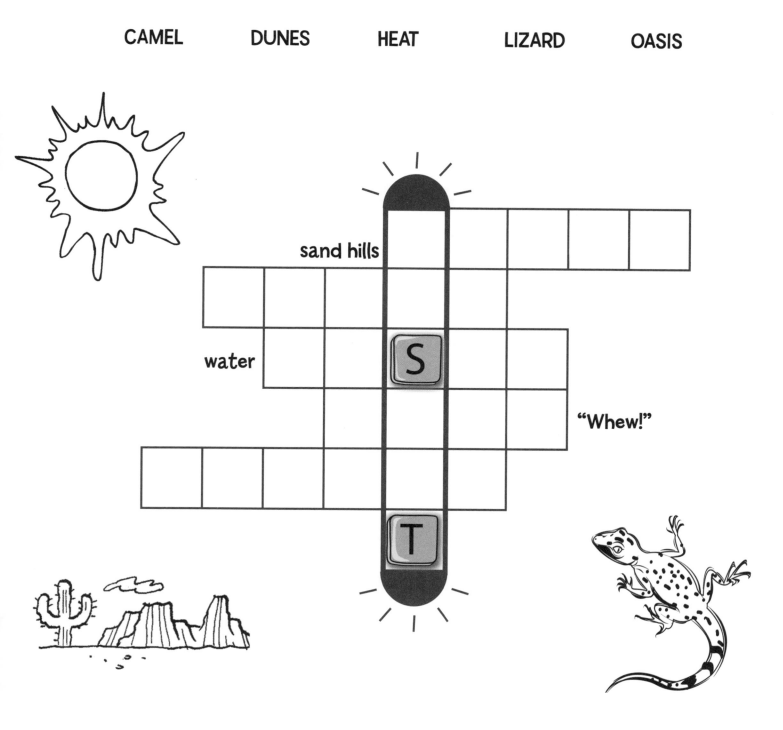

sand hills

water

"Whew!"

X Marks the Spot

Ahoy, matey! This is a maze with a twist. Instead of searching for a clear path to the finish, find the solid black line that leads to the buried treasure.

Answer on page 182

Outer Space

Every word listed is contained within the group of letters below. Words can be found in a straight line diagonally, horizontally, or vertically. They may be read either forward or backward.

ASTRONAUT

BIG DIPPER

EARTH

MERCURY

METEOR

MOON

ORBIT

PLANET

PLUTO

STAR

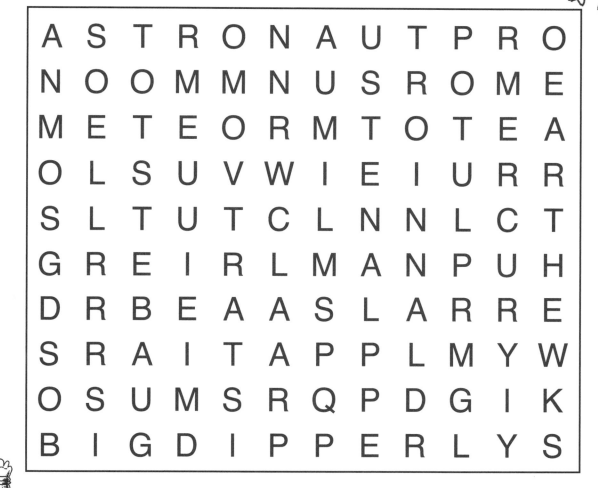

A	S	T	R	O	N	A	U	T	P	R	O
N	O	O	M	M	N	U	S	R	O	M	E
M	E	T	E	O	R	M	T	O	T	E	A
O	L	S	U	V	W	I	E	I	U	R	R
S	L	T	U	T	C	L	N	N	L	C	T
G	R	E	I	R	L	M	A	N	P	U	H
D	R	B	E	A	A	S	L	A	R	R	E
S	R	A	I	T	A	P	P	L	M	Y	W
O	S	U	M	S	R	Q	P	D	G	I	K
B	I	G	D	I	P	P	E	R	L	Y	S

Did you know?

Earth's atmosphere does not end suddenly, but gets thinner and thinner. About 67 miles above Earth, the atmosphere is 99 percent gone. About 100 miles above Earth, satellites can orbit Earth. At that point, true space may be said to begin.

Answer on page 182

Theme Park

This "ride" has a theme, but we can't tell you what it is. Place all the words in the boxes below—when you do, read the word created in the outlined boxes, from top to bottom, to reveal the theme.

ASTEROID   JUPITER   MERCURY   PLUTO   SUN

EARTH   MARS   MOON   SATURN   URANUS

VENUS

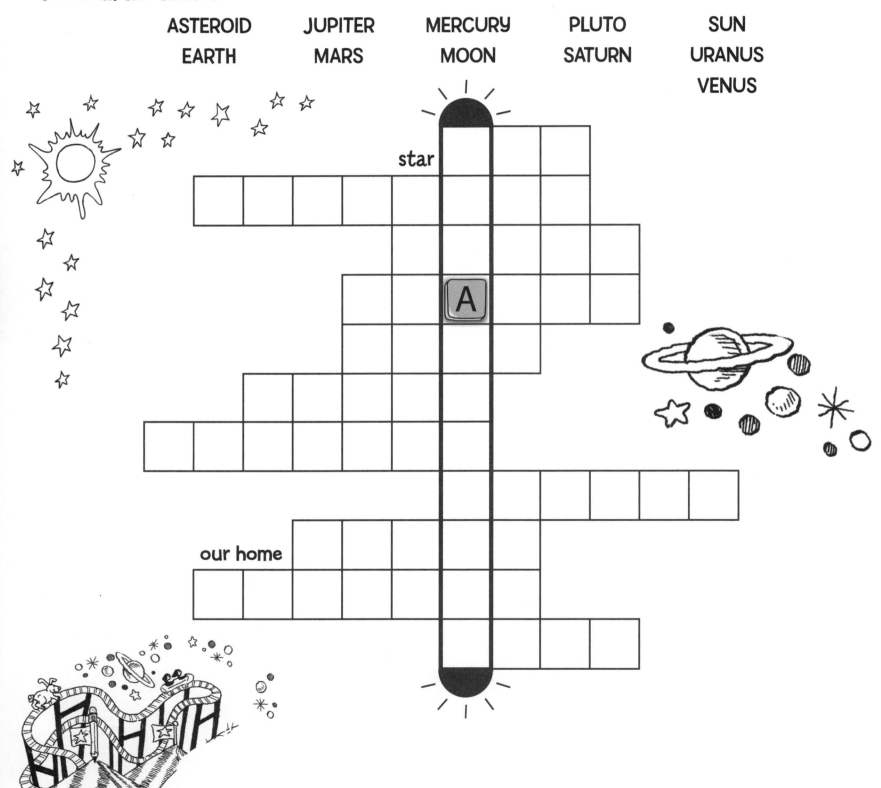

star

our home

Answer on page 182

Come Together

Place each of the tile sets into the empty spaces below to create 3 nine-letter American cities. Each tile set is used only once.

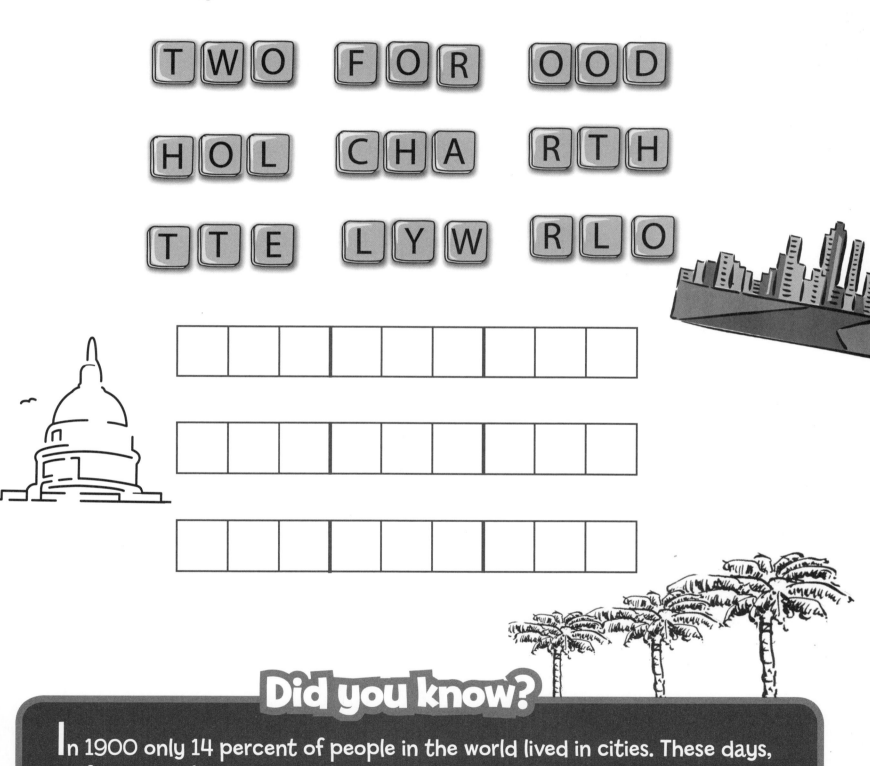

TWO   FOR   OOD

HOL   CHA   RTH

TTE   LYW   RLO

Did you know?

In 1900 only 14 percent of people in the world lived in cities. These days, half the world's population lives in cities!

Answer on page 182

Leapin' Lava

Watch out for molten lava on your way to the volcano.

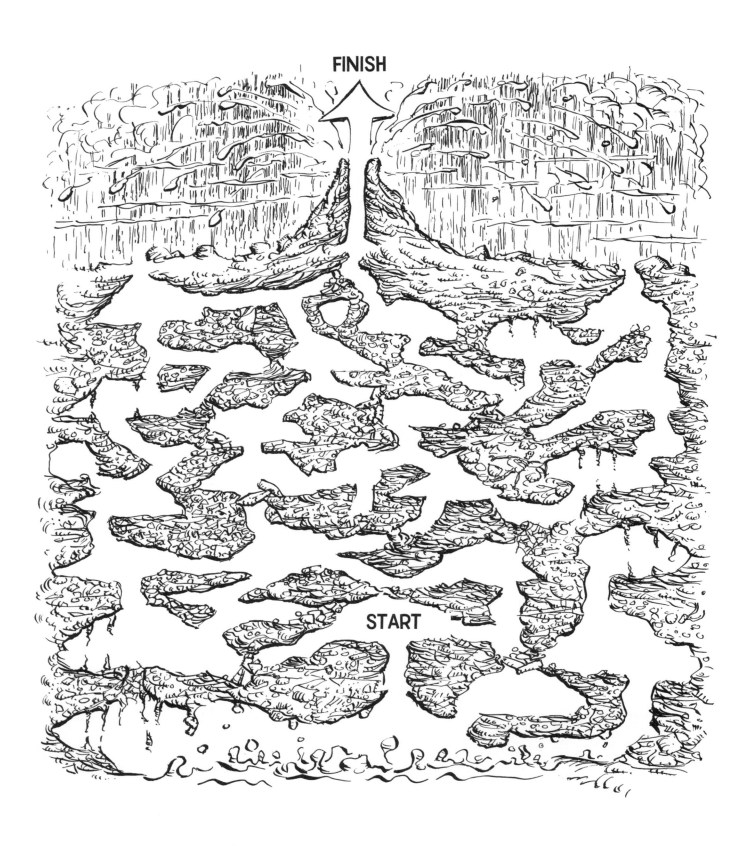

84

Answer on page 182

Piles of Tiles

Place all the tiles into the grid so they spell Canadian-themed words. The tiles are compiled in specific groups—those groups will appear together in across or down entries.

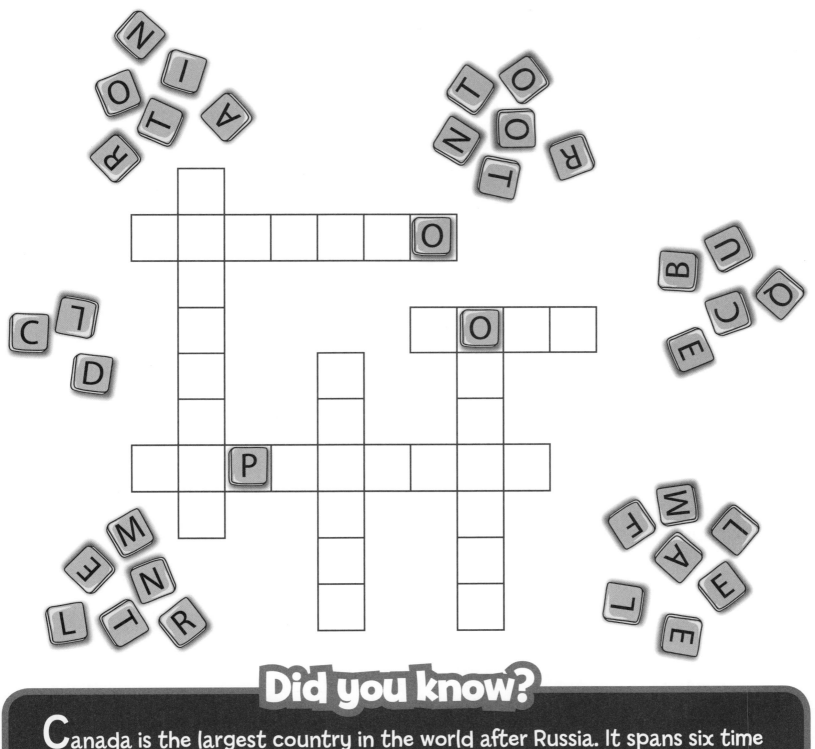

Did you know?

Canada is the largest country in the world after Russia. It spans six time zones and borders three oceans.

European Countries

Every word listed is contained within the group of letters below. Words can be found in a straight line diagonally, horizontally, or vertically. They may be read either forward or backward.

AUSTRIA

BRITAIN

FRANCE

GERMANY

GREECE

IRELAND

ITALY

MALTA

ROMANIA

SPAIN

SWEDEN

SWITZERLAND

TURKEY

E	C	E	E	R	G	S
F	R	A	N	C	E	P
W	S	D	A	D	R	A
L	W	N	T	N	M	I
Y	G	A	L	A	A	N
S	C	L	A	L	N	I
R	W	R	M	E	Y	A
O	Y	E	K	R	U	T
M	L	Z	D	I	A	I
A	A	T	G	E	V	R
N	T	I	N	C	N	B
I	I	W	Q	V	N	E
A	U	S	T	R	I	A

Answer on page 183

Gold Rush!

There's gold in this hill! Reach the gold nugget in the center of this maze (G) by traveling only through connecting white squares, and then get to "Out" safely, avoiding obstacles along the way. Hazards include fires, quicksand, chasms, and ponds. There's no backtracking, and you cannot advance on black squares.

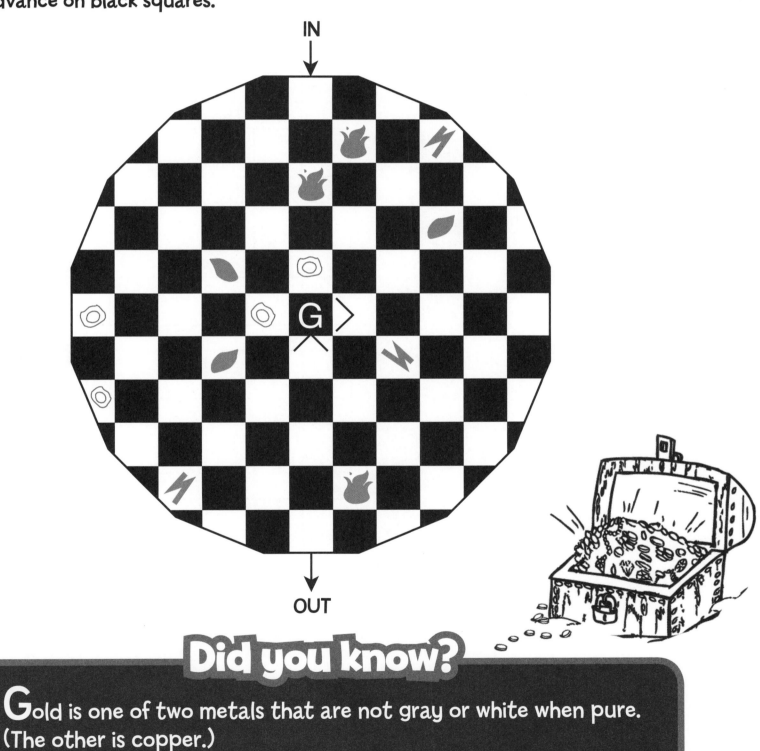

Did you know?

Gold is one of two metals that are not gray or white when pure. (The other is copper.)

Answer on page 183

Add-a-Letter

Rearrange the tiles from each word, adding one new tile from the bottom in order to form the names of world capitals in the empty boxes. Each tile from the bottom of the page is used only once.

Answer on page 183

Secret Spaces

These eight objects are hidden somewhere in the picture. Can you find and circle them all?

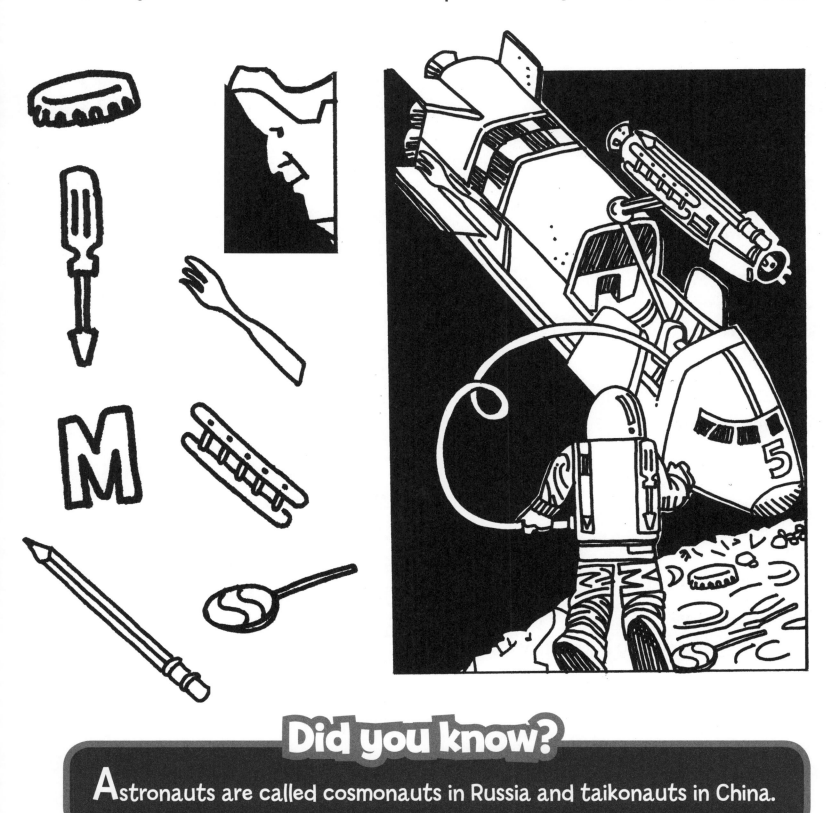

Did you know?

Astronauts are called cosmonauts in Russia and taikonauts in China.

Answer on page 183

Outer Space

ACROSS

1. Our star
4. Points: abbr.
7. Space Shuttle launchers: abbr.
8. Weaver's machine
10. "_____ as I say!"
11. What water becomes when it's boiled
13. Stomach muscle, for short
15. Once _____ blue moon
17. _____ Francisco, California
18. Historical time
19. Fly or sing alone
21. Do, _____, mi, . . .
22. Fireplace residue
23. _____ and outs
25. _____ and feathers
    (old-time punishment)
27. Highest card
29. Alphabet beginning
31. Long-_____ roses
34. Peter _____ (flying boy in the movies)
35. Place to take a bath
37. A magician may pull a rabbit
    out of one
38. Extraterrestrial: abbr.

39. _____ module (moon buggy)
41. Shortstop: abbr.
42. Part of a galaxy
44. _____ and address
46. Possess
47. Place to exercise

DOWN

1. South America: abbr.
2. The _____ Enterprise
   (Star Trek vessel)
3. Baseball's Nationals, for short
4. Mercury or Venus, for example
5. Male cat or turkey
6. "Not _____ fast!"
7. Something that's forbidden
9. The Red Planet
10. Talk trash to
12. Serving of corn
14. "_____, humbug!"
16. Creature from another world
18. Our planet
20. Ham _____ rye
24. Planet with rings

26. "_____ a matter of fact..."

27. Gorilla or chimp

28. Lions and tigers are big ones

30. Hot dog or hamburger bread

32. "...with the greatest of _____"

33. Mountains: abbr.

36. Big _____ (formation of the universe, in theory)

39. Attorney's field

40. Bit of sunlight

43. From top _____ bottom

45. Millimeter: abbr.

Did you know?

Some galaxies contain as many as a trillion stars. The smaller galaxies may have fewer than a million stars.

Answer on page 183

Crossed Out

Use the given tiles to spell a pair of related words that meet on the given letter.

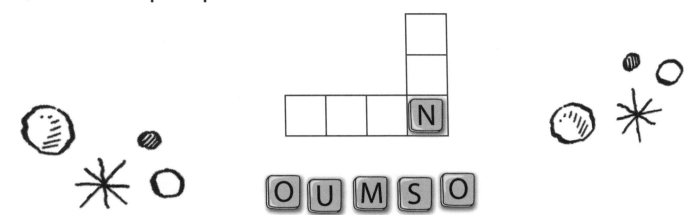

| | |
|N| |

O U M S O

Did you know?

For thousands of years, different peoples around the world have used the sun, moon, and stars as the basis of timekeeping.

Crossed Out

Use the given tiles to spell a pair of words with opposite meanings that meet on the given letter.

O

E R L C A

N I G F L

Answer on page 183

Car Chase

These people have had a great day shopping in the city! One problem: They can't find the parking garage to get their car. Can you help?

Tile Tie-Ins

Using the letter tiles below, complete the grid to reveal the names of 12 states.

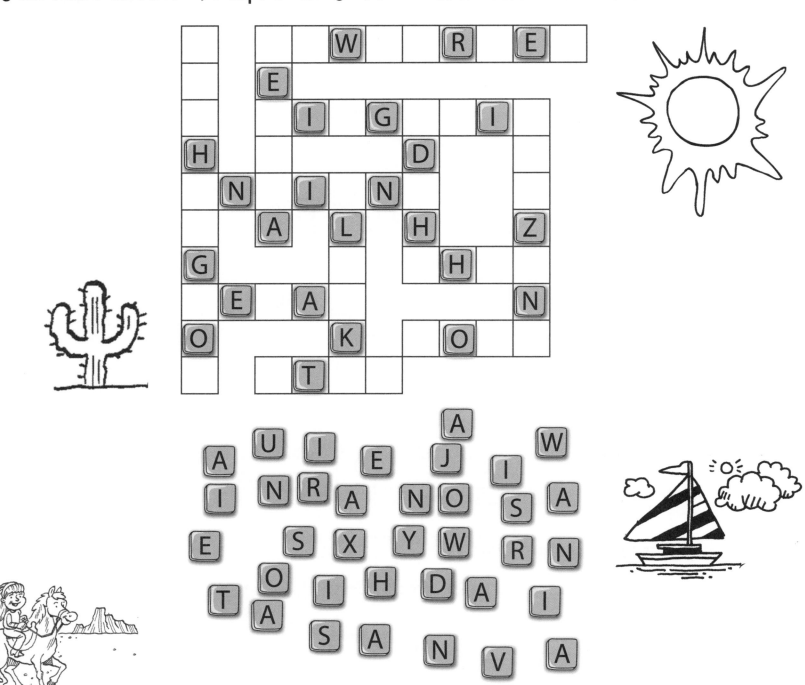

Did you know?

Arizona, California, Nevada, New Mexico, Texas, Utah, and parts of Colorado used to be part of Mexico. Mexico lost this territory to the US in 1848.

Answer on page 184

Follow the Trail

Follow the correct trail to get to the top of the mountain. Travel over and under bridges if necessary.

FINISH

START

Come Together

Place each of the tile sets into the empty spaces below to create 3 nine-letter countries. Each tile set is used only once.

ONE   AND   HUA

IND   NIA   ZIL

SIA   LIT   SWA

Did you know?

One of the answers is among the smallest countries in Africa and is almost completely surrounded by the country of South Africa.

Answer on page 184

Picture-by-Number

Shade in the numbers that are divisible by 7. Once complete, you will reveal a simple image.

37	2	34	86	50	3	48	21	4	25	69	17	78	60	6
5	74	15	75	40	19	77	57	91	72	39	45	89	66	2
8	92	66	46	94	84	88	26	47	49	67	36	65	59	97
78	17	75	46	63	65	79	49	12	94	49	34	67	88	94
15	64	78	14	46	11	56	32	98	16	43	35	38	37	79
1	64	86	70	65	63	75	93	78	49	44	98	92	38	31
76	93	4	35	13	70	48	88	38	35	59	21	20	2	66
20	93	68	14	51	6	14	82	56	88	60	21	39	48	41
43	16	8	56	33	41	47	35	55	83	74	70	4	65	52
67	36	8	49	17	57	89	76	92	61	87	56	57	46	22
66	11	59	70	36	65	37	67	4	71	22	35	46	75	78
52	18	28	14	45	89	48	55	78	17	80	14	56	61	15
44	98	41	35	48	8	96	63	33	83	51	21	54	91	3
56	30	64	70	58	94	84	82	56	80	85	7	43	50	77
42	81	62	28	55	47	42	95	98	6	82	77	16	48	14
28	54	97	98	32	79	35	85	21	31	68	63	31	50	70
7	38	83	56	8	39	7	30	70	33	13	21	39	23	77
42	67	7	7	84	98	84	82	77	35	56	35	84	86	91
63	98	68	86	18	68	91	32	77	18	38	17	95	56	7
21	47	79	94	10	45	30	70	90	18	81	9	66	37	70

Piles of Tiles

Place all the tiles into the grid so they spell major US cities. The tiles are compiled in specific groups—those groups will appear together in across or down entries.

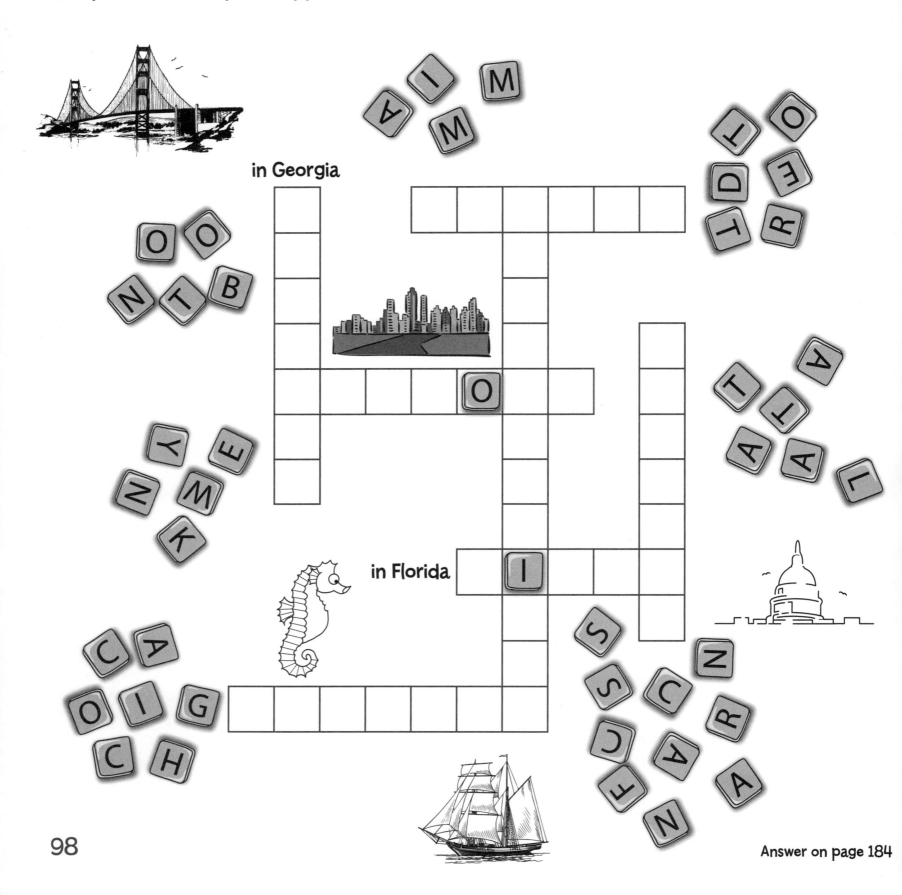

in Georgia

in Florida

98

Answer on page 184

Tile Tie-Ins

Using the letter tiles below, complete the grid to reveal 12 world capitals.

Did you know?

One of these capitals is known as the Eternal City and is more than 3,000 years old.

USAnagrams

Unscramble the letters to discover the names of five states in the United States. Once you've done this, match the states with their capitals.

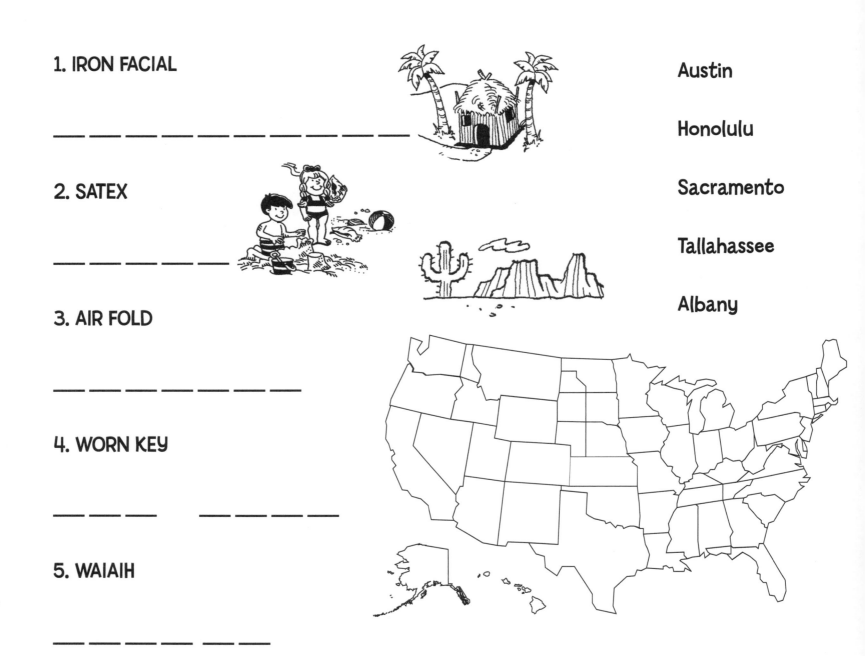

1. IRON FACIAL

__ __ __ __ __ __ __ __ __ __

2. SATEX

__ __ __ __ __

3. AIR FOLD

__ __ __ __ __ __ __

4. WORN KEY

__ __ __ __ __ __ __

5. WAIAIH

__ __ __ __ __ __

Austin

Honolulu

Sacramento

Tallahassee

Albany

Did you know?

New York City isn't its state's capital, but it served as the first capital of the United States until 1790.

Answer on page 184

Road Map Mystery

Follow each person's path on the map of town, and answer the questions below.

1. Who visited the post office at least twice?

2. Who went from the bank to the hospital?

3. Who visited the most places?

4. Where did Bill go between the hospital and school?

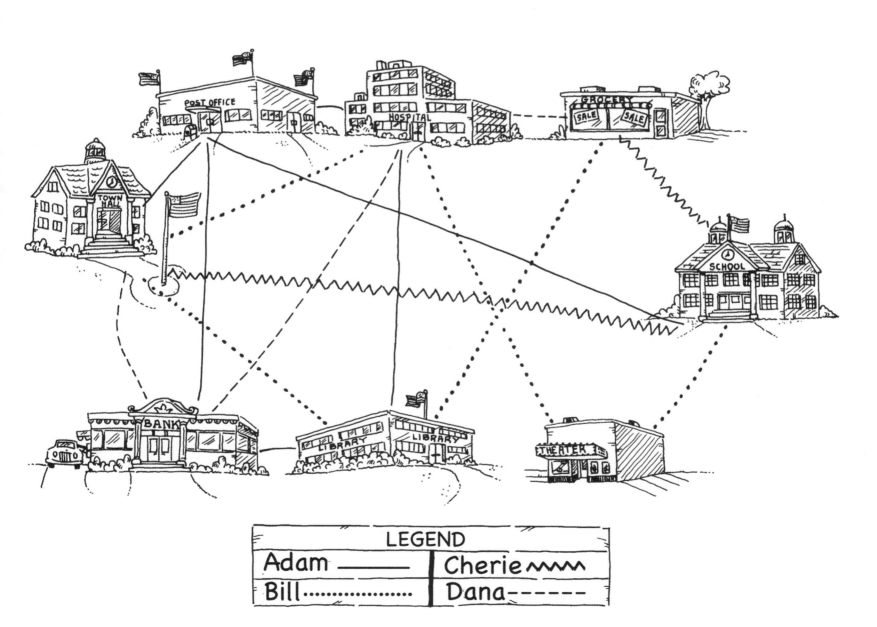

LEGEND	
Adam ————	Cherie ⋀⋀⋀
Bill ··········	Dana — — — —

Answer on page 184

Sarah's Desert

Help Sarah and Sugarfoot find their way through the desert to Cactus Creek.

102

Answer on page 184

Geography Anagrams

Rearrange the letters in parentheses to spell the names of five different countries. The poem may offer you some help!

Should you feel an Irish wind,

You might be standing in _____ (RED NAIL).

You won't find koalas in Canada;

You'll have to journey to _____ (AS A RITUAL).

While vacationing in _____ (GRAY MEN),

The autobahn you're sure to see.

Culinary knowledge you'll likely gain

When you visit and dine in _____ (I SNAP).

San Francisco has the Golden Gate

Here in the _____ (ATTEND TISSUE).

Did you know?

Ancient Hebrew writers may have first invented anagrams. Some used arrangements of words and letters to seek new meanings in poetry and prayer.

Outer Space

Answer the clues with words that will fit on the lines. Then, find those answers in the grid on the next page. Words can be found in a straight line horizontally, vertically, or diagonally. They may be read either forward or backward.

1. This is located in the vast region between Mars and Jupiter.

   — — — — — — — —
   — — — —

2. What kind of person rides in the space shuttle?

   — — — — — — — — —

3. This is often bright in the night sky and has a long "tail."

   — — — — — —

4. Our own planet!

   — — — — —

5. What is the name of the biggest planet in our solar system?

   — — — — — — —

6. This planet is nicknamed the "Red Planet."

   — — — —

7. Which planet is closest to the sun?

   — — — — — — —

8. What is the name of our own galaxy? Hint: It's also the name of a candy bar!

   — — — — —   — — —

9. What heavenly body did Neil Armstrong first walk on in July 1969?

   — — — —

10. What is the name of the vivid blue, windy eighth planet in our solar system?

    — — — — — — —

Did you know?

Nicolaus Copernicus, in 1543, was the first person to state that the planets travel around the sun.

Answer on page 185

11. Which dwarf planet used to be considered the ninth planet in our solar system?

— — — — —

12. What provides signals for television, radio, GPS, and many other modern technologies?

— — — — — — — — —

13. What planet is known as the "Ringed Planet"?

— — — — — —

14. This is the collective name for the sun and everything that revolves around it.

— — — — — —

— — — — — —

15. Which planet is located just after Saturn, in terms of distance from the sun?

— — — — — — —

16. Which planet is closest in size to our own? (It's about 94.9 percent the size of Earth.)

— — — — — —

```
T Q U K N H Y T N N R U T A S
U A B P Y P C E W E O T U L P
A Z S M P Y X M J U P I T E R
N E X T E T H O D C W T D E Y
O T Z S E V L C Y Q S H U M P
R I Q N L R C T P P G T E N O
T L S A H Y O S U N A R U V E
S L P B W N B I O F C A V D N
A E P I M B U Q D U M E I B R
G T N A V Q T L R B N H M W G
M A R M T A S Y W U E G S I V
M S R M E T S Y S R A L O S I
O Y A W Y K L I M T D A T G A
O B B Y C A G M T T O W E B K
N U B L A O T F F K T R P R J
```

Number Code: States

First, solve each of the arithmetic problems. Then, find the corresponding letter in the number code at right. Write the letter for that number on the second dash. Reading down the column of letters will reveal the hidden words.

❶ $12 \div 2 =$ ___ ___

$33 \div 3 =$ ___ ___

$20 \div 4 =$ ___ ___

$40 \div 20 =$ ___ ___

$24 \div 6 =$ ___ ___

❷ $30 \div 5 =$ ___ ___

$56 \div 7 =$ ___ ___

$14 \div 7 =$ ___ ___

$65 \div 5 =$ ___ ___

$99 \div 9 =$ ___ ___

$8 \div 4 =$ ___ ___

$44 \div 4 =$ ___ ___

❸ $24 \div 4 =$ ___ ___

$88 \div 8 =$ ___ ___

$36 \div 4 =$ ___ ___

$36 \div 2 =$ ___ ___

$75 \div 3 =$ ___ ___

$55 \div 5 =$ ___ ___

$26 \div 13 =$ ___ ___

$63 \div 3 =$ ___ ___

❹ $48 \div 8 =$ ___ ___

$40 \div 8 =$ ___ ___

$35 \div 5 =$ ___ ___

$18 \div 6 =$ ___ ___

$50 \div 10 =$ ___ ___

$34 \div 2 =$ ___ ___

$77 \div 7 =$ ___ ___

$34 \div 17 =$ ___ ___

❺ $60 \div 10 =$ ___ ___

$45 \div 9 =$ ___ ___

$36 \div 3 =$ ___ ___

$48 \div 4 =$ ___ ___

$72 \div 9 =$ ___ ___

$30 \div 2 =$ ___ ___

$72 \div 8 =$ ___ ___

$60 \div 12 =$ ___ ___

CODE

1.	F	14.	V
2.	N	15.	U
3.	H	16.	Z
4.	E	17.	G
5.	I	18.	Y
6.	M	19.	W
7.	C	20.	X
8.	O	21.	D
9.	R	22.	Q
10.	P	23.	J
11.	A	24.	K
12.	S	25.	L
13.	T	26.	B

Did you know?

The letter M probably started as a picture sign of water in Egyptian hieroglyphic writing and in early Semitic writing.

Answer on page 185

Word Web

It's a crossword without clues! Place the state capitals into the grid to complete the puzzle. There's only one solution.

ATLANTA (GA)

AUGUSTA (ME)

AUSTIN (TX)

BOISE (ID)

BOSTON (MA)

CONCORD (CT)

HELENA (MT)

JACKSON (MS)

JUNEAU (AL)

LANSING (MI)

LINCOLN (NE)

MADISON (WI)

PIERRE (WA)

RALEIGH (SC)

SALEM (OR)

TOPEKA (KS)

TRENTON (NJ)

Answer on page 185

ART AND ATHLETICS

Sports and arts are some of the types of fun activities people do based on their interests. Since ancient times people have run races, wrestled, and hunted for sport. Ancient people in many parts of the world also played games with balls. As for art, people have been drawing since prehistoric times. Prehistoric people drew on cave walls, on rocks, and probably on sand. Today, individual arts are often grouped into categories such as performing arts, literature, and visual art.

Word Swatter

Use three letters from the words below to create eight common words. Letters will be used more than once but will not repeat in each word.

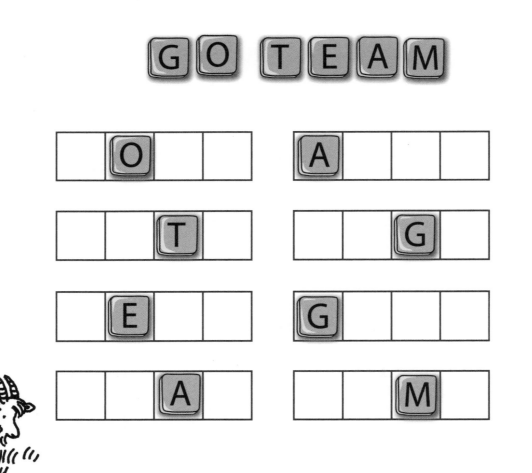

GO TEAM

Answer on page 185

Home Run!

Follow the slugger's blast to the ball in the center of the maze and then out of the park.

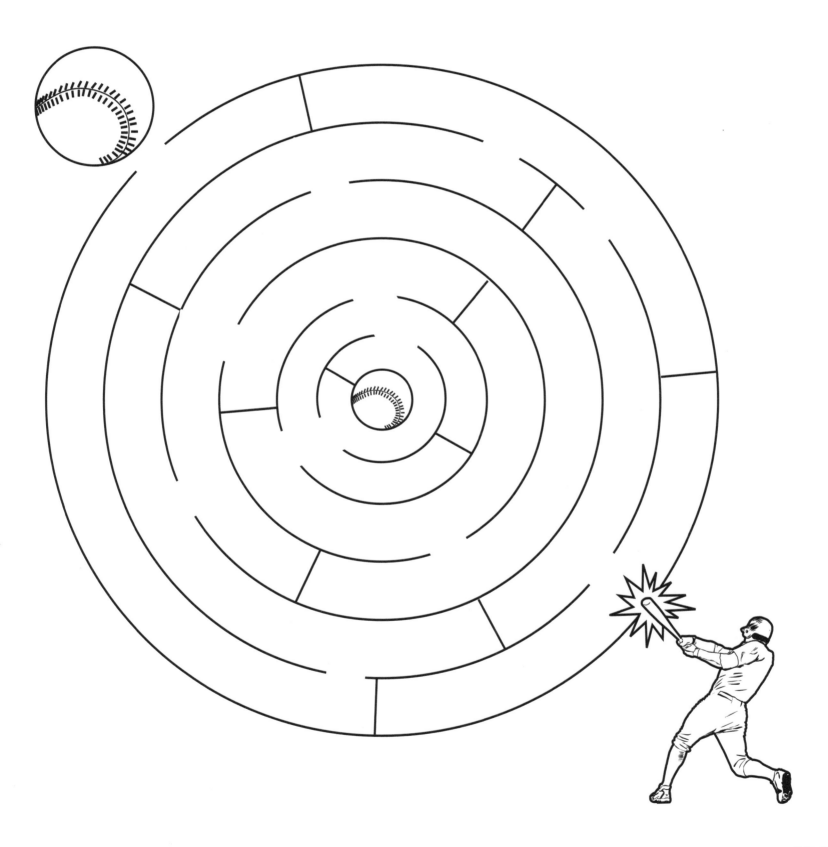

Report Card

Anthony just received his first report card at his new fine-arts middle school. Determine the grade Anthony got in each subject. He got two As, two Bs, and one C.

1. His creative writing grade is better than his drawing grade.

2. He didn't get an A in digital arts.

3. He did better in drawing than he did in theater.

4. He got an A in music.

	A	B	C
Creative Writing			
Digital Arts			
Drawing			
Music			
Theater			

Answer on page 185

Decoder

Use the code below to reveal the answer to this riddle.

Q: Where did the golf gear go after a long day?

A =   B = ✴   C = ◗   D = ✜   E = ❖

F = ✺   G = ✽   H = ✗   I = ◎   J = ➹

K = ◡   L = ⅋   M = ❊   N = ⊕   O = ⋇

P = ✳   Q = ✦   R = ‖   S = ()   T = ⚡

U = (dumbbell)   V = ⊙⊙   W = ■   X = ◡   Y = ☉

Z = 8

_ _ _   _ _ _ _ _ _ _ _ _!

Did you know?

The Native American soldiers known as code talkers played a key role in the Allied victory in World War II. They transmitted sensitive wartime messages by speaking their native languages, in effect using them as a code.

Number Code: Sports

First, solve each of the math problems. Then, find the corresponding letter in the number code to the right. Write the letter for that number on the second line. Reading down the column of letters will reveal the hidden words.

1
9 + 5 = ___ ___
11 + 11 = ___ ___
3 + 2 = ___ ___
5 + 5 = ___ ___
7 + 2 = ___ ___
6 + 7 = ___ ___

2
19 + 4 = ___ ___
13 + 9 = ___ ___
4 + 1 = ___ ___
2 + 3 = ___ ___
3 + 6 = ___ ___
14 + 5 = ___ ___

3
17 + 6 = ___ ___
4 + 2 = ___ ___
11 + 10 = ___ ___
12 + 6 = ___ ___
21 + 2 = ___ ___
8 + 6 = ___ ___

4
4 + 3 = ___ ___
4 + 14 = ___ ___
8 + 15 = ___ ___
1 + 8 = ___ ___
6 + 1 = ___ ___
13 + 5 = ___ ___
10 + 2 = ___ ___
7 + 5 = ___ ___

5
9 + 3 = ___ ___
2 + 16 = ___ ___
2 + 3 = ___ ___
11 + 8 = ___ ___
14 + 8 = ___ ___
12 + 11 = ___ ___
13 + 10 = ___ ___
3 + 6 = ___ ___

CODE

1.	F	14.	H
2.	G	15.	X
3.	I	16.	D
4.	M	17.	J
5.	C	18.	A
6.	Q	19.	R
7.	B	20.	N
8.	T	21.	U
9.	E	22.	O
10.	K	23.	S
11.	Z	24.	W
12.	L	25.	V
13.	y	26.	P

Did you know?

A jib, a chock, a cleat, and a skeg are all parts of a sailboat.

Answer on page 185

Gone Fishin'

Grab your tackle box and get to the other side of the riverbank.

Hoops Commute

Four friends get on the same bus every morning to go to basketball practice. Each one lives on a different street and gets on the bus at a different stop. Determine the street name where each friend gets on the bus and the order in which they are picked up in the morning.

1. Sara isn't the first on the bus. Marcia lives on a Street not a Road.

2. Patti is the fourth to be picked up.

3. Emily doesn't live on East Street.

4. The girl who gets on the bus first lives on West Street.

5. Sara doesn't live on South Road.

6. The friend who lives on North Road is picked up before Sara but after Marcia.

Name	Street	Order
Emily		
Marcia		
Patti		
Sara		

	East Street	North Road	South Road	West Street	1st	2nd	3rd	4th
Emily								
Marcia								
Patti								
Sara								
1st								
2nd								
3rd								
4th								

Answer on page 185

Picture This

Copy the picture in each numbered square into the same numbered square in the grid to reveal some things your imagination might get lost in.

	A	B	C
1			
2			
3			

Did you know?

Drawing is a form of art. It is also the starting point for painting, sculpture, and other art forms.

Answer on page 186

Piles of Tiles

Place all the tiles into the grid so they spell some camping-related words. The tiles are compiled in specific groups—those groups will appear together in across or down entries.

yummy

shelter

Did you know?

The majority of people who camp drive to their campsites. However, others travel to campsites in remote areas far from the road by hiking, canoeing, horseback riding, or skiing there.

Answer on page 186

Riddle in the Middle

Use the clues to complete the five-letter answers, starting at the top and working your way down. When finished, read the letters in the squares with the thick boxes, from top to bottom, to reveal the answer to the riddle below.

Q: What makes it possible for a basketball player to jump higher than a house?

1. Theater employee U [ ] R

2. Near C [ ] E

3. Cursor mover M [ ] E

4. Brim of a cap V [ ] R

5. Steering device W [ ] L

6. Squander W [ ] E

7. Duck-hunter's lure D [ ] Y

8. Georgia fruit P [ ] H

9. Twist or tango D [ ] E

10. Very ornate F [ ] Y

11. Not tall S [ ] T

12. Halloween character W [ ] H

13. Army rank M [ ] R

14. Edge of a pizza C [ ] T

15. Punctuation mark C [ ] A

16. Give money back R [ ] Y

Snack Attack

The man with the snacks in the upper-right corner needs a little assistance avoiding obstacles so he can get back to his seat in the bleachers and enjoy the game. Can you help him?

Answer on page 186

Reword Rewind

Unscramble the tiles to form words that will complete the sentence.

The athlete wanted to for shoes

to make her and leaps higher.

Word Swatter

Use three letters from the words below to create four common words. Letters will each be used more than once but will not repeat in each word.

A PLUS

   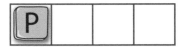

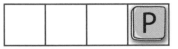   

Did you know?

In less than two years, American track and field athlete Gail Devers went from being seriously ill with Graves disease to winning an Olympic gold medal. She was three times the world champion in the 100-meter hurdles.

Answer on page 186

Theme Park

This "ride" has a theme, but we can't tell you what it is. Place all the words in the boxes below—when you do, read the word created in the outlined boxes, from top to bottom, to reveal the theme.

BOOTS

BUNNY SLOPE

GLOVES

LIFT

MOUNTAIN

OUTFIT

POLES

SNOWBOARD

for your feet

learn here

W

K

up, up and away

for your hands

Answer on page 186

Add-a-Letter

Rearrange the tiles from each word, adding one new tile from the bottom in order to form things related to ice hockey in the empty boxes. Each tile from the bottom of the page is used only once.

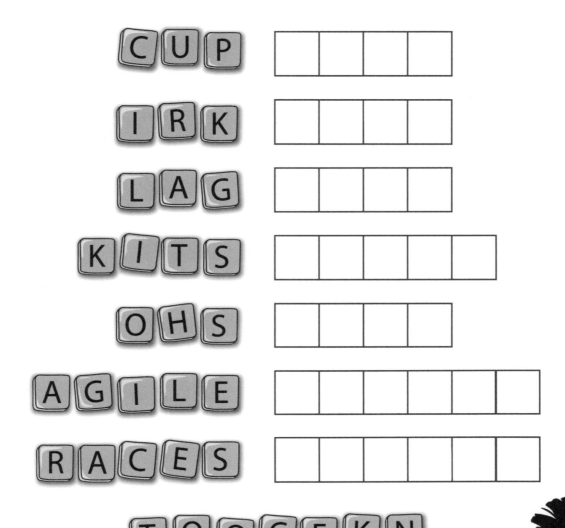

Did you know?

The fastest of all team sports, ice hockey has been described as a combination of "blood, sweat, and beauty."

Answer on page 186

Jammin'!

Can you spot the eight rockin' differences between these two cool band scenes?

Did you know?

This band is playing bluegrass instruments—can you spot a banjo, a mandolin, and a fiddle? Bluegrass is an American music style that came into being in the 1940s. It is descended from string-band music from even earlier times.

Answer on page 186

Decoder

An old notebook was recently dug up in a baseball field. Use the code below to decipher the two riddles and their answers that are written in the book.

W[H]RE DO WE [F]IN[D] [P]I[R][A]TE[S] THAT [D]ON'T [S]A[I]L [S][H]I[P]S, CA[R]R[Y] S[W]O[R][D]S, OR [B]U[R][Y] [T][R]EA[S][U]RE?

ANSWER: [P]I[T][T]S[B]U[R][G]H, [P]A

* * *

[W]HER[E] D[O] WE F[I][N]D [D]I[A][M]O[N]D[B]A[C][K]S THAT ARE [R][E]D AND [B][A][L][C]K, LI[V][E] IN THE [D]E[S]ERT, BUT DON'T [H]AVE ANY [R][A]T[T][L][E]S?

ANSWER: A[R]I[Z][O][N]A

A = ♣   B = 🍎   C = ⚜   D = 🖌   E = ✴

F = ⊱   G = 👓   H = 💡   I = 🧷   J = 🐦

K = ✂   L = 🔒   M = 📺   N = 🔑   O = ☎

P = 🔨   Q = ✳   R = 🧦   S = 🔓   T = ⊰

U = ⏰   V = 👔   W = 🏏   X = 🛁   Y = 🥄

Z = ➹

Answer on page 186

Class Schedule

Olivia is imagining her ideal school. Help her make up an imaginary class schedule.

1. Olivia has camping right after kickball.

2. Her last class is surfing.

3. She has swimming later in the day than photography.

4. During second period, Olivia studies dance.

5. She doesn't have kickball third period.

	1	2	3	4	5	6
Camping						
Dance						
Kickball						
Photography						
Surfing						
Swimming						

Did you know?

In the mid-1800s, Horace Mann, the "father of the American public school," pioneered the concept that education should be available to everyone, non-religious, and free. He was also strongly anti-slavery and a champion of rights for workers and for women.

Answer on page 187

THEME PARK

This "ride" has a theme, but we can't tell you what it is. Place all the words in the boxes below—when you do, read the word created in the outlined boxes, from top to bottom, to reveal the theme.

CLARINET

CYMBALS

DRUM

FLUTE

HORN

OBOE

SAXOPHONE

TROMBONE

TRUMPET

TUBA

VIOLIN

slide

oom pah!

rat-a-tat-tat

T

Tile Tie-Ins

Practice the art of science! Using the letter tiles below, complete the grid to reveal 10 elements from the periodic table.

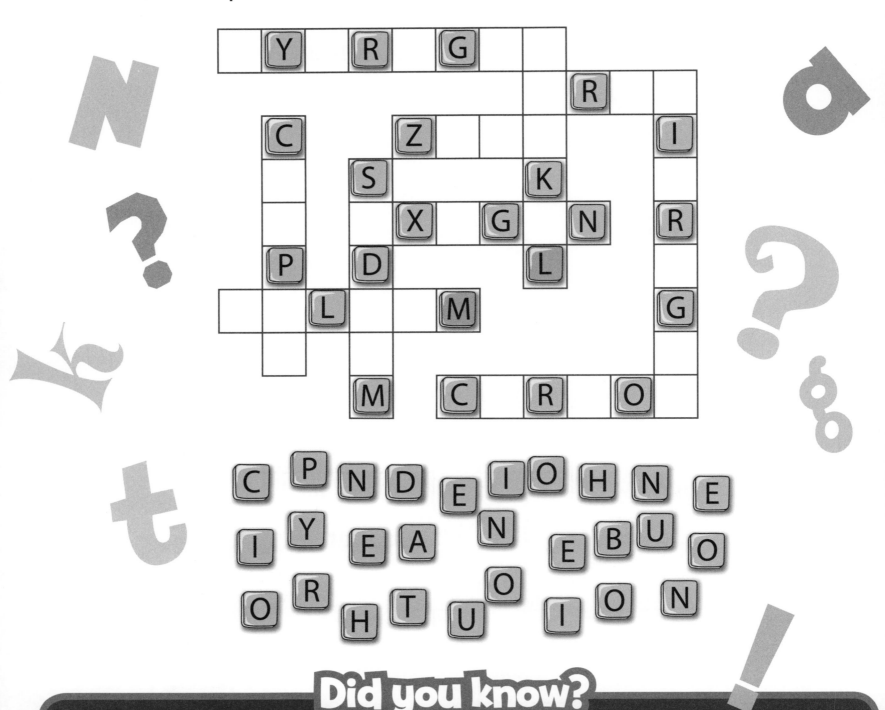

Did you know?

There are 92 chemical elements found in nature. Scientists have created more than 20 additional elements.

Answer on page 187

Rockin' Road

Which guitar will lead to the amp below? Find out if you want to be a rock star!

Add-a-Letter

Rearrange the tiles from each word, adding one new tile from the bottom tiles in order to form a type of sport in the empty boxes. Each tile from the bottom of the page is used only once.

LOG

LOP

STEIN

SCORE

BURG

CHERRY

YNAFCO

Did you know?

In some ancient cultures, sports were a part of religious practices. The ancient Greeks played in the Olympics to honor their gods. The popularity of the games was so great that the four-year period between games became a means of recording time.

Answer on page 187

Sketchbook

Natalia sketched everything she saw yesterday in her sketchbook. Later on, she erased three of the drawings and replaced them with three new drawings. Study the top picture carefully, then turn the page upside down and study the revised sketchbook page. Without looking back at the first picture, can you circle the three drawings that are different?

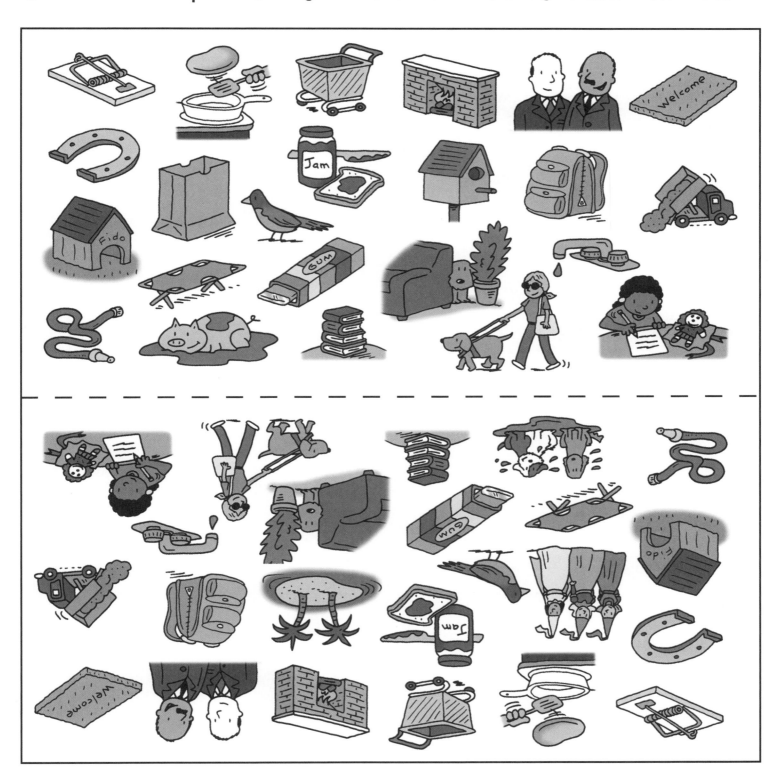

Word Ladder

Can you change just one letter on each line to transform the top word to the bottom word? Don't change the order of the letters, and make sure you have a common English word at each step.

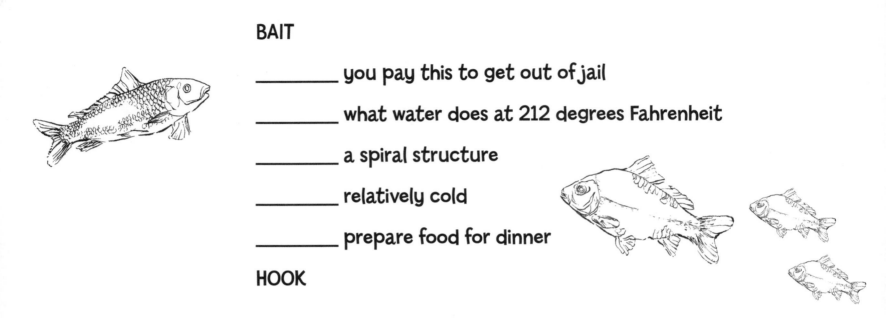

BAIT

_____ you pay this to get out of jail

_____ what water does at 212 degrees Fahrenheit

_____ a spiral structure

_____ relatively cold

_____ prepare food for dinner

HOOK

Word Swatter

Use three letters from the words below to create eight common words. Letters will be used more than once but will not repeat in each word.

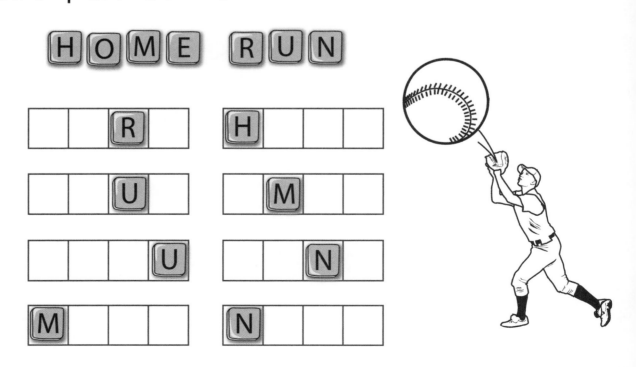

H O M E R U N

		R	
		U	
		U	
M			

H			
M			
		N	
N			

Answer on page 187

Tangled Kites

Can you help the kids find their own kites?

Did you know?

Inventors of early airplanes based many of their ideas on kites.

Mathletes Meeting

ACROSS

1. Close friend
4. The total of
7. Find the total of
10. Our land: abbr.
11. "_____ Little Teapot"
12. Space between teeth
13. Times _____ (math memorization)
15. Flash _____ (math drill aids)
17. "Do _____ I say!"
18. "Yes," in Spain or Italy
19. Spaghetti, macaroni, etc.
22. Mathematical average
26. Alley _____ (basketball pass)
27. Stomach muscles, for short
29. Huge bird ridden by Sinbad
30. Number you can't divide by
32. Having the same value
34. Number approximately equal to 3.14159
36. You and me
37. $3 \times 3 \times 3 = 3$ _____
40. Remains of a campfire
44. The result of a number divided by itself
45. Corn portion
47. "_____ had it up to here!"
48. Coffee or flower holder
49. Fruity drink
50. Morning moisture

DOWN

1. Shot _____ (track & field event)
2. "Strong _____ bull"
3. Science classroom: abbr.
4. "Nap," in Mexico
5. Sound of hesitation
6. Apple computers
7. Agriculture: abbr.
8. Male parent
9. Double plays: abbr.
14. _____ Vegas, Nevada
16. "Ready, _____, fire!"
19. "The Raven" poet Edgar Allan _____
20. Fourth month: abbr.
21. "Honest _____" Lincoln
23. Period in history
24. One of the first email providers
25. North Carolina: abbr.
26. Ounces: abbr.
28. Figure with four equal sides and four equal angles
31. Open, in poetry
33. Star Trek vessel, the _____ Enterprise
35. "What's the big _____?"
37. Policeman
38. Card game with Skip and Reverse cards
39. Put chips in a pot
41. Stayed out of sight
42. New Year's _____
43. Do some stitching
46. Help wanted _____

1	2	3		4	5	6		7	8	9
10				11				12		
13			14			15	16			
			17			18				
	19	20			21		22	23	24	25
26				27		28		29		
30			31		32		33			
			34	35		36				
37	38	39				40		41	42	43
44				45	46			47		
48				49				50		

Did you know?

In the ninth century an Arab mathematician named al-Khwarizmi described a problem-solving system that is now known as algebra.

Picture This

Copy the picture in each numbered square into the same numbered square in the grid to reveal something to help you rock on!

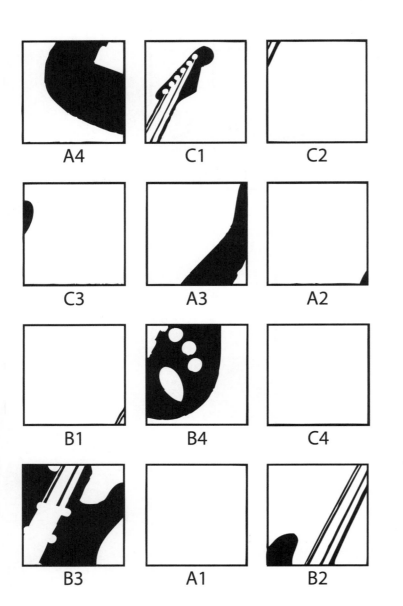

	A	B	C
1			
2			
3			
4			

Did you know?

Dictionary makers, governing officials, and even fans and performers have a very difficult time defining what, exactly, "rock music" is. Go ahead—give it a try!

Answer on page 188

Walking Trail

This hiker is tired and lost. Help him get back to his campsite.

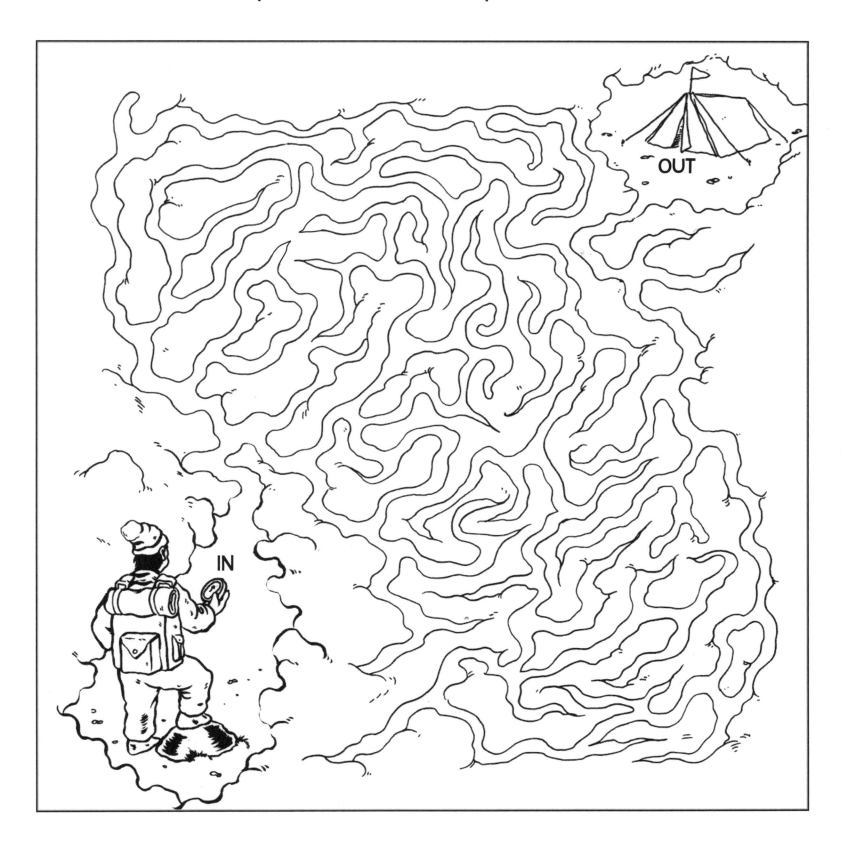

America's Pastime

ACROSS

1. Face the pitcher
4. Designated hitter: abbr.
6. Iron-_____ (some decals)
9. _____-two-three inning (inning with no baserunners)
10. Split _____ soup
11. Butter or oil
12. Swipe a base
14. Southpaw
16. South America: abbr.
17. The Dodgers' city: abbr.
18. Baseball shoes
22. Right-handed pitcher: abbr.
25. Touch with the baseball
26. Enjoy a hot dog at the ballpark
28. Rowing instrument
30. _____ fly (easy chance for an infielder)
32. Three-base hit
34. One _____ the other
36. Air conditioning: abbr.
37. Try to avoid a tag
40. Fake duck
44. "Very funny!" on social media
45. Easter egg coloring
47. "_____ you sure?"

48. Hooting bird
49. The Padres' city: abbr.
50. Where relief pitchers warm up, for short

DOWN

1. City of the Red Sox: abbr.
2. _____ farm (hobby kit with insects)
3. Very young Little Leaguers bat off this
4. Delaware: abbr.
5. Cooperstown's National Baseball _____ of Fame
6. On/_____ switch
7. Washington ballplayer, for short
8. Pig pen
10. Home _____ (place on a baseball diamond)
13. "_____ matter of fact…"
15. Hearing organ
18. Connecticut: abbr.
19. Once around the track
20. Conceited person's problem
21. Rode the bench
23. Bad _____ (tricky chance for an infielder)
24. Good buddy
27. Exchange of players between teams
29. Do, _____, mi, …
31. Peas holder

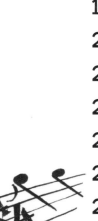

33. Hockey surface

35. Cincinnati's team

37. _____-mo replay

38. Like a pitched ball below the knees

39. Not feeling well

41. Ballplayer's headwear

42. Unrefined metal

43. Japanese money

46. Yard: abbr.

Did you know?

A book published in 1928 described a game called rounders that was very similar to modern baseball. One big difference was that an outfielder who picked up a ground ball was supposed to try to hit the runner with the ball!

Answer on page 188

Picture-by-Number

Shade in the numbers that are divisible by 12. Once complete, you will reveal a simple image.

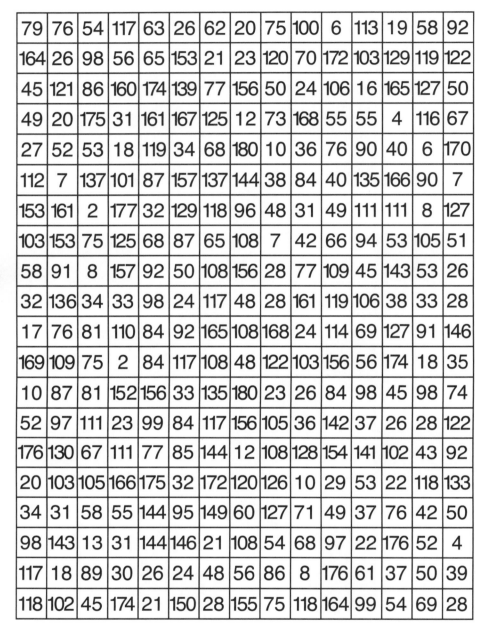

79	76	54	117	63	26	62	20	75	100	6	113	19	58	92
164	26	98	56	65	153	21	23	120	70	172	103	129	119	122
45	121	86	160	174	139	77	156	50	24	106	16	165	127	50
49	20	175	31	161	167	125	12	73	168	55	55	4	116	67
27	52	53	18	119	34	68	180	10	36	76	90	40	6	170
112	7	137	101	87	157	137	144	38	84	40	135	166	90	7
153	161	2	177	32	129	118	96	48	31	49	111	111	8	127
103	153	75	125	68	87	65	108	7	42	66	94	53	105	51
58	91	8	157	92	50	108	156	28	77	109	45	143	53	26
32	136	34	33	98	24	117	48	28	161	119	106	38	33	28
17	76	81	110	84	92	165	108	168	24	114	69	127	91	146
169	109	75	2	84	117	108	48	122	103	156	56	174	18	35
10	87	81	152	156	33	135	180	23	26	84	98	45	98	74
52	97	111	23	99	84	117	156	105	36	142	37	26	28	122
176	130	67	111	77	85	144	12	108	128	154	141	102	43	92
20	103	105	166	175	32	172	120	126	10	29	53	22	118	133
34	31	58	55	144	95	149	60	127	71	49	37	76	42	50
98	143	13	31	144	146	21	108	54	68	97	22	176	52	4
117	18	89	30	26	24	48	56	86	8	176	61	37	50	39
118	102	45	174	21	150	28	155	75	118	164	99	54	69	28

Did you know?

Musicians have developed a system for writing down music so that others can play it again. They use certain symbols, called notes, to indicate the tones to be played or sung. Early examples of musical notation date from the days of ancient Greece.

Answer on page 188

Lunchtime Logic

Every day, six friends sit together for lunch in the cafeteria. They always sit in the same places, and three always bring their lunch while the other three always buy lunch. Determine the name of each friend, her position at the table (use the diagram below) and whether each brings or buys her lunch.

1. The three friends who bring their lunches are Emily, the friend who sits in Seat D, and the friend who sits in Seat E.

2. Emily has only one person sitting beside her. The person in Seat C buys her lunch.

3. Amy has a person sitting on both sides. Holly only has one person sitting beside her, but she isn't in Seat D.

4. Valerie sits in Seat F. Trudy sits beside Holly but not beside Stacy.

5. Stacy brings her lunch.

	A	B	C
		Table	
	D	E	F

Name	Position	Lunch

	Seat A	Seat B	Seat C	Seat D	Seat E	Seat F	buys	brings
Amy								
Emily								
Holly								
Stacy								
Trudy								
Valerie								
buys								
brings								

Picture This

Copy the picture in each numbered square into the same numbered square in the grid to uncover a breezy activity.

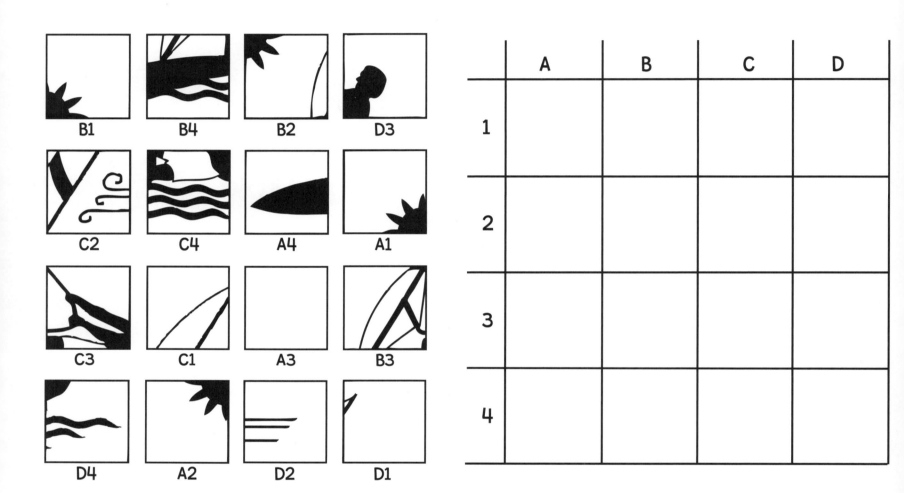

Did you know?

The pictured activity is a combination of two other activities and was invented in the US by Hoyle Schweitzer and Jim Drake in 1967.

Answer on page 188

Track Club

In track club yesterday, everyone ran a mile. Determine the first and last names of the five runners and their times for running a mile.

1. The five runners, from fastest to slowest, were Matthew, the person whose last name is Wakefield, Tina, the person who ran the mile in eight minutes, and the person whose last name is West.

2. Sam ran the mile one minute faster than Jake.

3. Elsie's last name isn't Grant.

4. The person whose last name is Smith ran the mile one minute faster than Sam, whose last name isn't Parker.

	Grant	Parker	Smith	Wakefield	West	5 minutes	6 minutes	7 minutes	8 minutes	9 minutes
Elsie										
Jake										
Matthew										
Sam										
Tina										
5 minutes										
6 minutes										
7 minutes										
8 minutes										
9 minutes										

First Name	Last Name	Time

Answer on page 188

TECH AND TRANSPORT

Throughout history, technology has made people's lives easier. One area where technology has played an essential role is transportation. The world's economy depends on transportation. Raw materials must be moved to factories. Then products must be moved from factories to stores.

People need transportation, too. Just as they have for thousands of years, people today rely on walking to travel short distances. For longer distances, people use animals, bicycles, cars, trucks, trains, ships, airplanes, and more.

Crossed Out

Use the given tiles to spell a pair of words with opposite meanings that meet on the given letter.

Answer on page 189

Add-a-Letter

Rearrange the tiles from each word, adding one new tile from the bottom in order to form a type of transportation in the empty boxes. Each tile from the bottom of the page is used only once.

OUT

OIL

TAB

DEAN

HIS

IRAN

O M T S P A

Fit It

Figure out the names for each of the modes of transportation below, then fit those names into the crossword grid.

ACROSS

DOWN

144

Answer on page 189

Nice Trike

Which tricycle is the mirror image of the one in the box?

A.

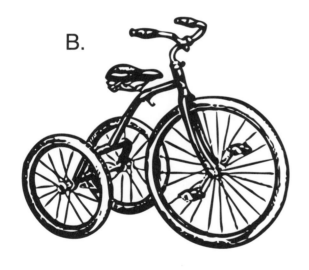

B.

C.

Did you know?

Scottish veterinary surgeon John Boyd Dunlop made a pneumatic tire for his son's tricycle in 1887. He went on to patent this invention, and he is known today as the inventor of the automobile tire.

Answer on page 189

Picture This

Copy the picture in each numbered square into the same numbered square in the grid to reveal this people-mover.

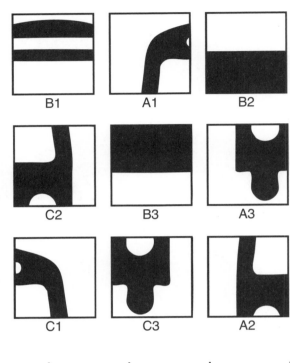

B1   A1   B2

C2   B3   A3

C1   C3   A2

	A	B	C
1			
2			
3			

Did you know?

Although robots in stories and movies often look human-like, real robots do not usually look like people.

Answer on page 189

Nuts and Bolts

Help the robot reach its missing parts!

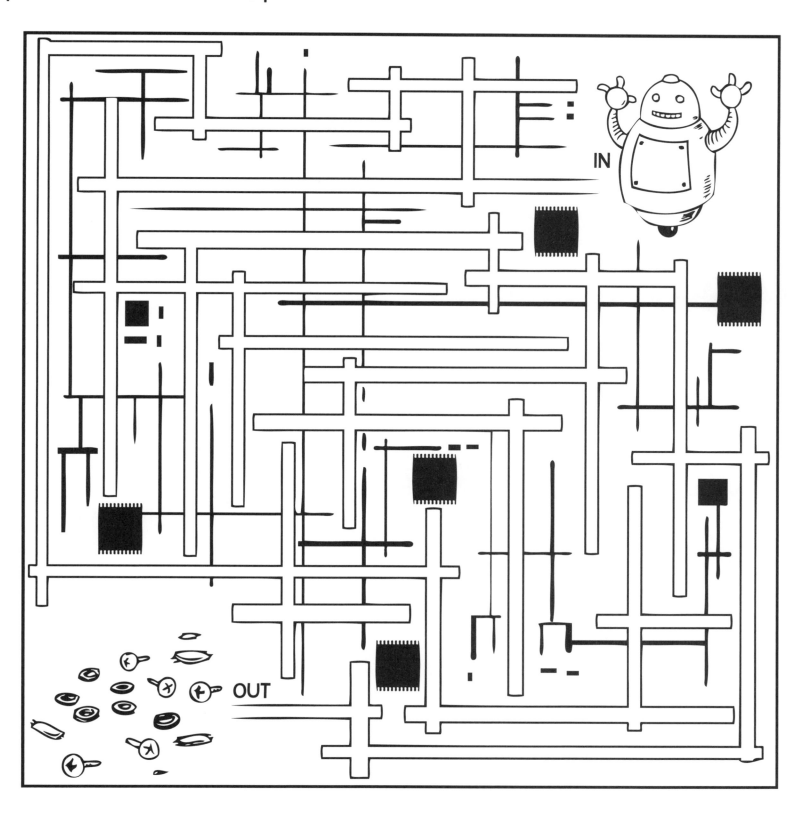

IN

OUT

Add-a-Letter

Rearrange the tiles from each word, adding one new tile from the bottom in order to form a type of tool in the empty boxes. Each tile from the bottom of the page is used only once.

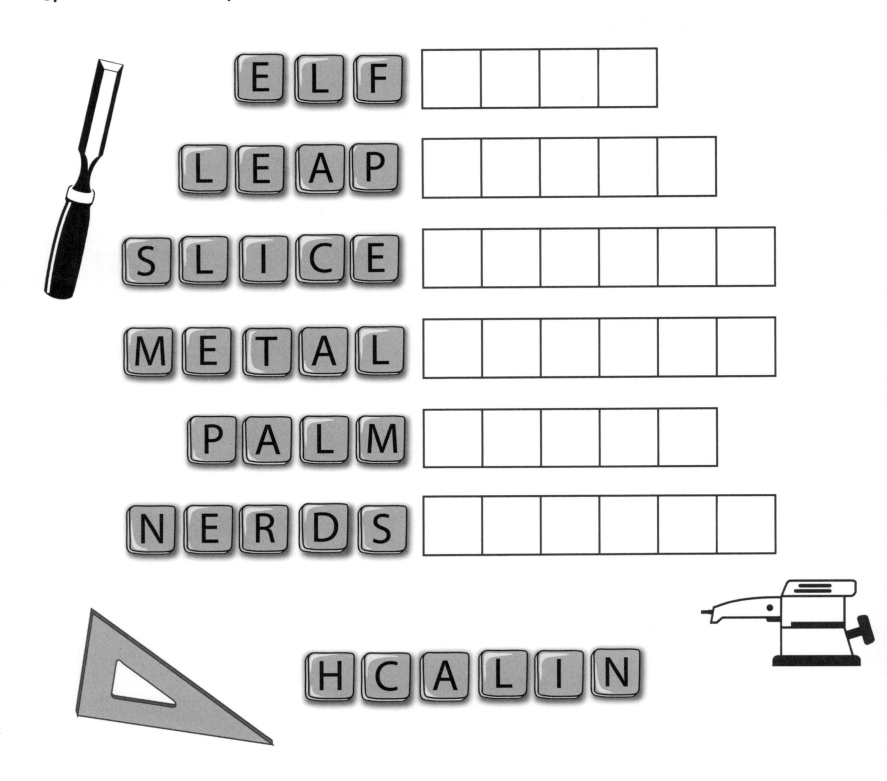

ELF

LEAP

SLICE

METAL

PALM

NERDS

HCALIN

148

Answer on page 189

Decoder

Use the code below to reveal the answer to this riddle: What did the computer say after the phone pinched him?

A = Ⰳ   B = §   C = ꓭ   D = Ψ   E = Ⲋ

F = ¶   G = ℧   H = ß   I = ✳   J = ‰

K = ⁑   L = ‡   M = Ж   N = ¥   O = Φ

P = ⱱ   Q = ¤   R = ≋   S = ◗   T = ∏

U = ɸ   V = ⊓   W = Δ   X = ⁎   Y = Ю

Z = Љ

T H A T   W A S   U N C A L L E D   F O R!

Did you know?

Alexander Graham Bell was the inventor of the electric telephone. On March 10, 1876, in Boston, the first sentence was successfully transmitted by telephone. The historic words were spoken to his assistant, Thomas Watson: "Mr. Watson, come here; I want you."

Answer on page 189

BRITANNICA KIDS BRAIN GAMES

Getting There

ACROSS

1. Transportation to school
4. "Friend or _____?"
7. Transportation that's hailed on city streets
10. "A penny saved _____ penny earned"
11. Et cetera: abbr.
12. President Lincoln, for short
13. Hiawatha's transportation
15. Cowboy's transportation
17. Road: abbr.
18. "Wanna make something _____ it?"
19. Covered _____ (pioneer transportation)
22. Cost of riding a bus or taxi
26. Tree fluid
27. Neither here _____ there
29. Moving company's transportation
30. It may be expressed in square miles
32. The silent member of the Seven Dwarfs
34. Los Angeles: abbr.
36. Connecticut: abbr.
37. Transportation that runs on rails
40. Arctic peoples' water transportation
44. Farm animal that eats slop
45. Easter egg coloring
47. Ginger _____ (soft drink)
48. Female sheep
49. "Ready, _____, go!"
50. Mother's Day month

DOWN

1. Popular brand of pen
2. Our country: abbr.
3. _____ Diego, California
4. Get nourishment from (2 wds.)
5. Overtime: abbr.
6. Sound bounceback, in a cave
7. Family transportation
8. Stomach muscles, for short
9. Honey-making insect
14. Organization: abbr.
16. "They're _____!" (racetrack cry)
19. Simple card game for two players
20. Gorilla or chimp
21. Say "yes" by moving your head
23. Avenue: abbr.
24. Bit of sunshine
25. _____ route (on the way)
26. South America: abbr.
28. Spaceman's transportation
31. "_____ Baba and the Forty Thieves"
33. Parent-teacher association: abbr.
35. "No ifs, _____, or buts!"
37. Fill in _____ blank
38. Use oars
39. How old you are
41. Orange Thanksgiving vegetable
42. Chicken _____ king
43. Item needed to open a lock
46. "Hear _____!" (words before a public announcement, once)

1	2	3		4	5	6		7	8	9
10				11				12		
13			14			15	16			
			17			18				
	19	20			21		22	23	24	25
26				27		28		29		
30			31		32		33			
			34	35		36				
37	38	39				40		41	42	43
44				45	46			47		
48				49				50		

Did you know?

The first paved road in the world is believed to have been built in about 2500 BCE in Egypt as an aid to the construction of the Great Pyramids.

Answer on page 189

Treasure Boat

There's only way to get to the treasure at the bottom of this boat—see if you can find it! Use the ladders to move from level to level.

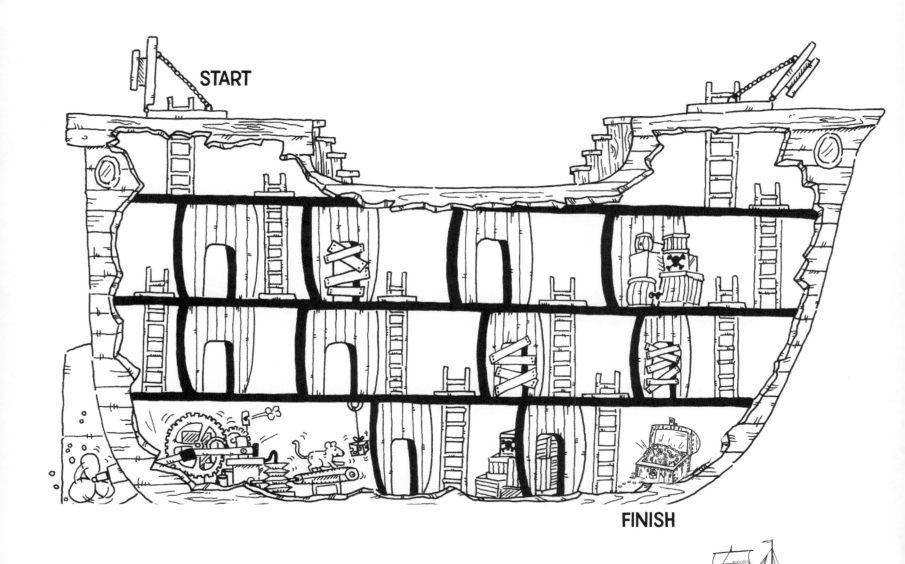

Did you know?

The speed at which a ship is moving is measured in knots. A knot is 1 nautical mile per hour. Pay attention—a nautical mile is not the same distance as a regular mile! One nautical mile is equivalent to 1.15 miles.

Answer on page 189

Picture This

Take this puzzle for a spin and copy the picture in each numbered square into the same numbered square in the grid.

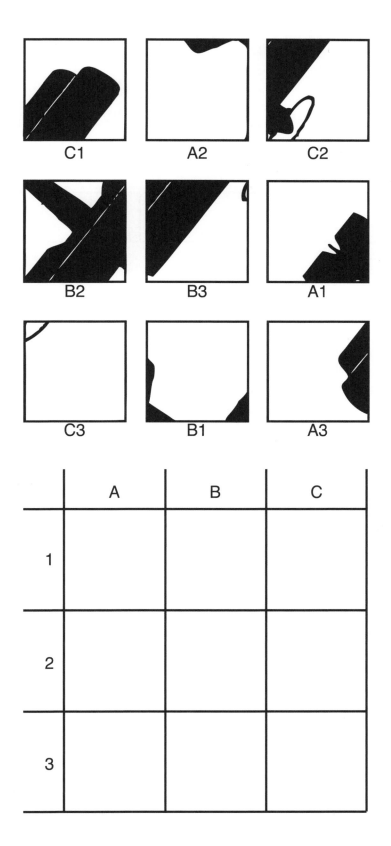

Piles of Tiles

Place all the tiles into the grid so they spell some high-flying terms. The tiles are compiled in specific groups—those groups will appear together in across or down entries.

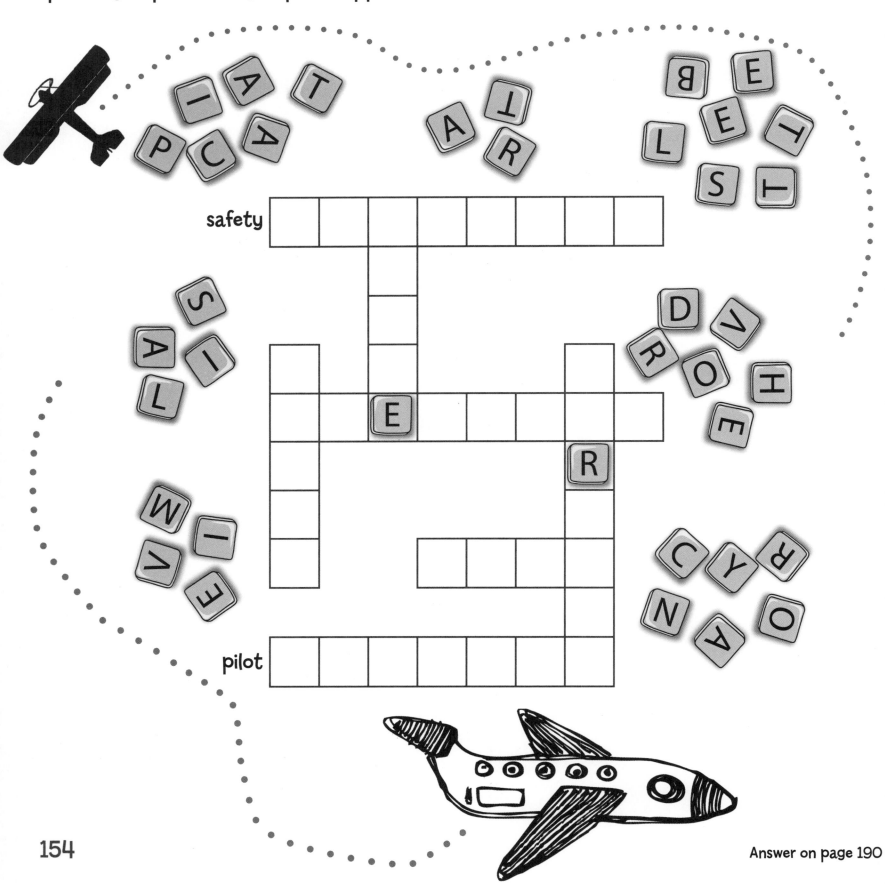

safety

pilot

154

Answer on page 190

Reword Rewind

Unscramble the tiles to form new words that will complete the sentence.

My biggest ☐☐☐☐ is not having

change for bus ☐☐☐☐ .

E A R F

Reword Rewind

Unscramble the tiles to form words that will complete the sentence.

The truck driver hauling pots and ☐☐☐☐ took

some ☐☐☐☐ to get rest before crossing the

bridges that ☐☐☐☐ the Mississippi River.

A P N S

Did you know?

More than 300 years before flying machines were perfected, Renaissance-era genius Leonardo da Vinci drew up plans for an airplane and a helicopter.

Answer on page 190

Lightbulb

Can you find your way through the tangled maze? Follow the electric path from points 1, 2, and 3 to turn on the lightbulb at the end to exit. It is OK to retrace your steps.

Did you know?

Light exists in two very different forms at the same time: it is both a particle and a wave.

Answer on page 190

All Aboard!

Can you spot the 10 differences between these two train station scenes?

Picture This

Copy the picture in each numbered square into the same numbered square in the grid to uncover one shipshape image!

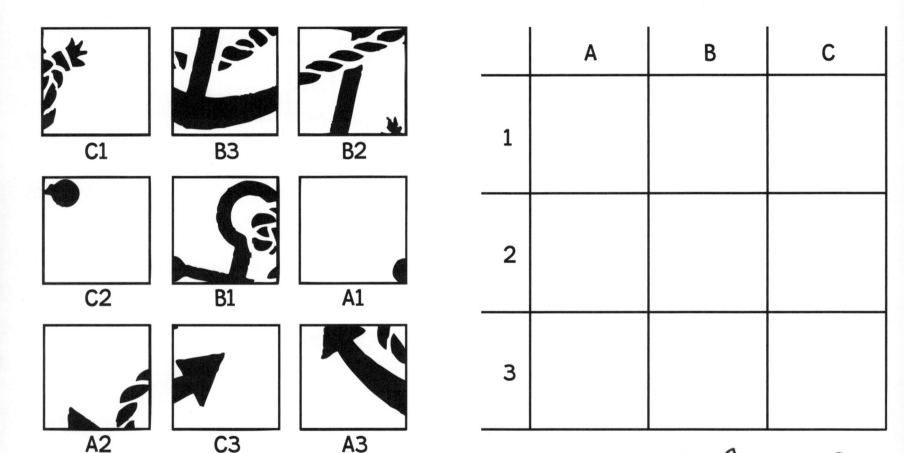

Did you know?

In 1996, archaeologists discovered the ship belonging to Blackbeard (Edward Teach) called the *Queen Anne's Revenge*, which sank off the coast of North Carolina in 1718.

Answer on page 190

Theme Park

This "ride" has a theme, but we can't tell you what it is. Place all the words in the boxes below—when you do, read the word created in the outlined boxes, from top to bottom, to reveal the theme.

CALL   FRIENDS   PARENTS
CASE   HOME   RINGTONE
EMERGENCY   LOL   TEXTING

letters

mom and dad [P]

help!

Picture-by-Number

Shade in the numbers that are divisible by 6. Once complete, you will reveal a simple image.

59	71	44	28	62	42	18	27	26	35	97	69
70	21	52	53	68	18	86	84	7	7	44	53
58	43	88	63	9	90	70	29	84	67	8	43
22	15	5	8	28	30	34	35	45	36	35	26
81	82	46	64	7	36	36	6	66	6	57	97
14	27	7	2	65	78	25	34	82	88	22	51
44	30	24	18	12	78	60	60	66	90	90	87
59	48	80	83	81	33	69	38	77	52	72	65
26	89	6	50	51	59	8	43	70	36	44	85
63	76	51	60	85	55	47	28	36	35	29	85
60	18	54	48	30	18	60	78	18	84	66	48
53	44	59	85	27	9	67	47	97	81	74	47

Answer on page 190

Getting There

Should you take a train, a boat, or a plane to arrive at your destination? Only one will get you there.

Did you know?

Bessie Coleman was the first African American aviator. Racial discrimination prevented her from entering aviation schools in the United States, so she learned French and earned her pilot's license in France in 1921.

Answer on page 191

Piles of Tiles

Place all the tiles into the grid so they spell terms related to the word "bicycle." The tiles are compiled in specific groups—those groups will appear together in across or down entries.

stop

for feet

Did you know?

There are twice as many bicycles as automobiles in the world, and they outsell automobiles three to one.

Answer on page 191

Riddle Scramble

Use the scrambled words to solve each of the clues below. Once you've done that, unscramble the letters found in the boxes to solve this riddle:

Q: I have a nose, tail, and wings, but I'm not a bird. What am I?

1. You can find me in this large building when I'm not working.

2. This machine allows me to move.

3. People pump thousands of gallons of this liquid into me.

4. I'm made of this shiny material.

5. I look like this animal.

6. This person is responsible for moving me.

7. You need this in order to get on me.

8. I carry these from city to city.

HAGRAN __ ☐ __ __ __ __

GEEINN __ __ __ __ ☐ __

FLUE __ __ ☐ __

ATELM __ __ __ ☐ __

DRIB __ __ ☐ __

LIPTO __ __ ☐ __ __

KITETC __ ☐ __ __ __ __

EELPOP ☐ __ __ __ __ __

☐ ☐ ☐ ☐ ☐ ☐ ☐ ☐

Find the Blocks

Find the shapes at the right in the grid as many times as listed. The shapes must be facing the same direction as the examples.

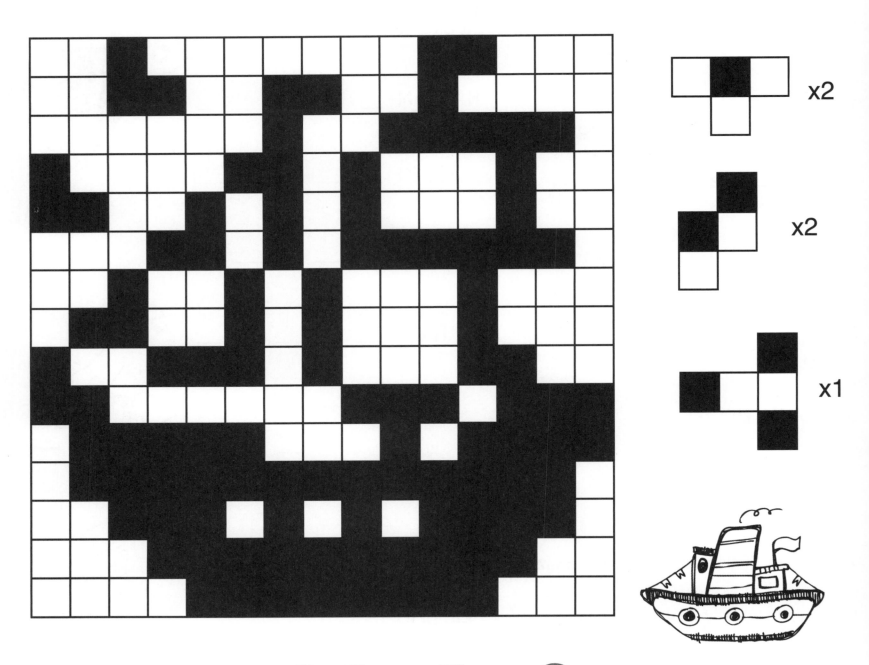

x2

x2

x1

Did you know?

Ship models displayed in museums are of great historical value. Many were originally made for purposes related to ship design.

Answer on page 191

Shoelaces

Match the laces to the shoes.

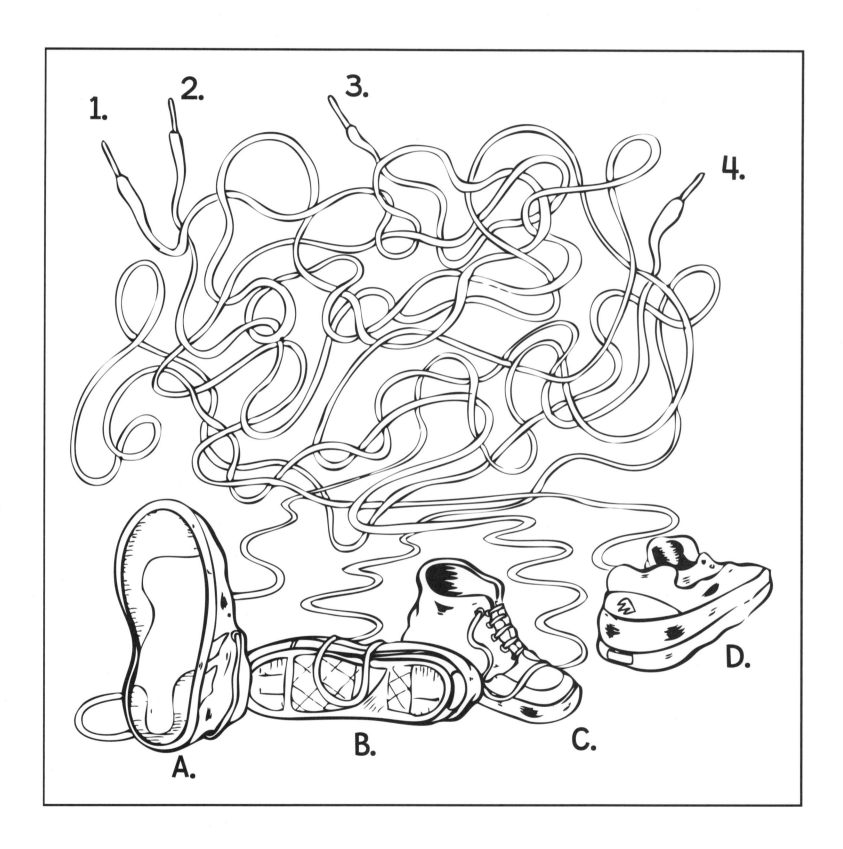

Word Ladder

Can you change just one letter on each line to transform the top word to the bottom word? Don't change the order of the letters, and make sure you have a common English word at each step.

WALK

_____ have a conversation

_____ a type of story

_____ a bargain price

_____ not any different

_____ a few

HOME

Word Swatter

Use five letters from the word below to create six common words. Letters will be used more than once but will not repeat in each word.

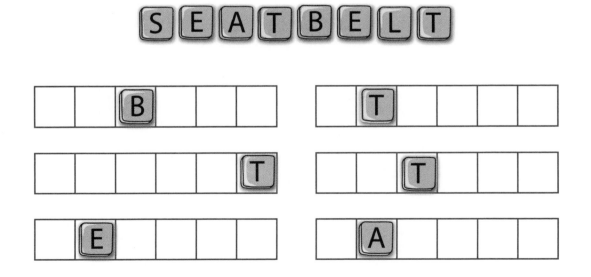

Answer on page 191

Chain Words

Place three letters in the middle squares that will complete one word and start another.
For example, TAR would complete GUI – TAR – GET.

| H | A | N | | | | A | G | E |

Did you know?

In the early days of aviation in the United States, pilots often used a cow pasture as a flying field and a barn for storing the plane.

Find the Blocks

Find the shapes at the right in the grid as many times as listed. The shapes must be facing the same direction as the examples.

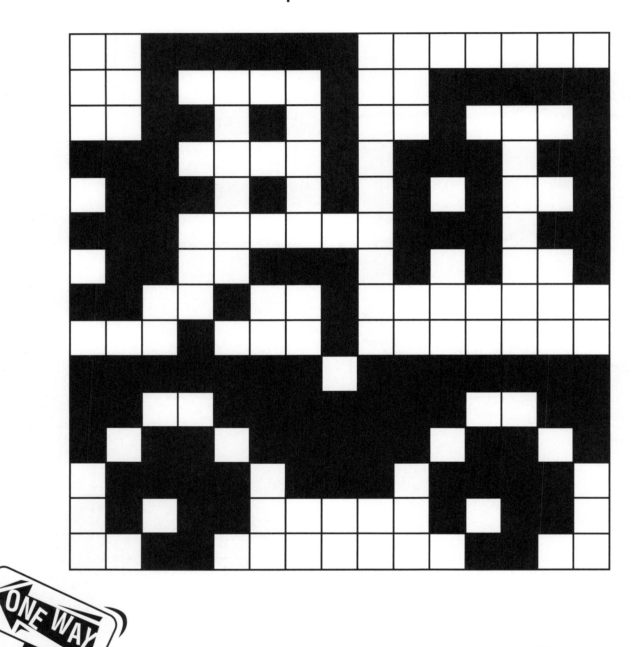

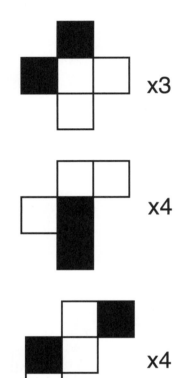

x3

x4

x4

Did you know?

The first true automobile had three wheels and was powered by steam. It was built by French inventor Nicolas-Joseph Cugnot in 1769, almost 140 years before Ford's first Model T!

Answer on page 191

Picture-by-Number

Shade in the numbers that are divisible by 11. Once complete, you will reveal a simple image.

150	90	38	134	114	7	92	36	14	2	153	5	67	10	158
106	61	20	42	48	93	77	154	110	124	46	111	61	148	151
85	114	46	113	158	88	133	95	39	55	103	123	139	158	123
65	42	84	63	154	29	126	126	1	56	88	81	145	125	129
61	57	85	121	68	37	59	40	120	94	94	88	149	36	2
124	114	99	97	9	24	26	124	1	101	85	140	110	86	42
13	79	22	115	120	112	105	47	152	21	116	152	110	5	6
20	25	154	1	7	90	160	8	59	119	39	6	22	158	73
131	139	11	3	101	105	140	42	151	21	71	39	33	152	125
144	152	143	89	7	107	123	95	148	115	14	24	132	133	90
130	122	22	95	31	73	109	8	28	36	74	51	154	94	52
81	65	156	55	89	23	105	101	114	71	87	22	90	79	87
26	123	150	119	55	80	145	153	81	159	99	51	6	130	159
30	80	131	50	11	58	126	144	53	7	33	130	73	123	139
53	131	16	89	19	55	17	103	155	121	64	90	5	47	6
39	30	43	117	134	66	14	96	145	110	15	38	86	155	40
76	57	146	9	122	59	55	22	110	37	156	41	136	25	6
27	25	80	46	151	154	132	77	88	88	155	139	126	56	101
46	106	76	48	52	158	154	121	66	101	115	9	59	54	127
90	79	8	134	123	14	102	98	46	70	23	127	81	16	20

Road Trip!

This confused driver is having trouble finding the gas station—and he's running on empty! Follow the arrows to help him find the correct route.

170

Answer on page 192

Find the Blocks

Find the shapes at the right in the grid as many times as listed. The shapes must be facing the same direction as the examples.

x4

x1

x2

Did you know?

The classic anchor shape pictured here was the model for many centuries, though nowadays people often use a different-shaped anchor that is easier to store.

Full Steam Ahead

Which engine is the mirror image of the one in the box?

A.

B.

C.

D.

E.

Did you know?

High-speed passenger trains were pioneered in Japan, which built the first high-speed rail in 1964. Today, high-speed commuter trains throughout Asia and Europe average more than 185 miles per hour.

Answer on page 192

Picture This

Copy the picture in each numbered square into the same numbered square in the grid, matey!

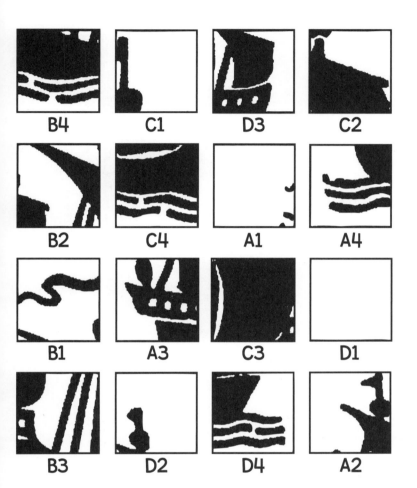

	A	B	C	D
1				
2				
3				
4				

Theme Park

This "ride" has a theme, but we can't tell you what it is. Place all the words in the boxes below—when you do, read the word created in the outlined boxes, from top to bottom, to reveal the theme.

PROP   SEATS

PILOT   REAR ENGINE

RUNWAY   WINDOWS

WINGS   MOTOR

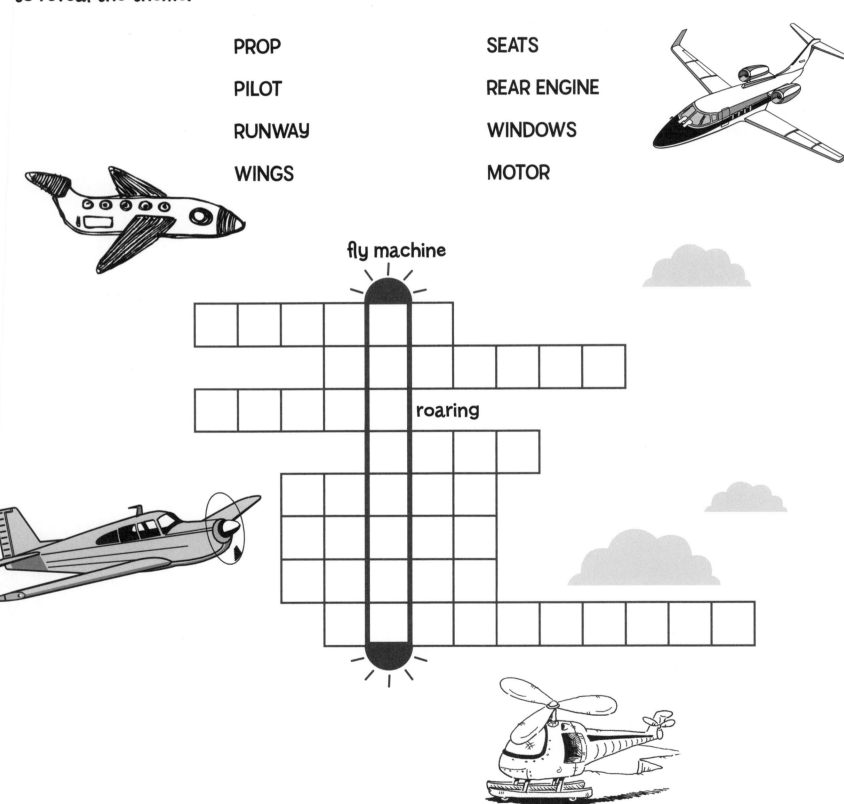

fly machine

roaring

Answer on page 192

Find the Animal (page 6)

snake

For the Birds (page 7)

```
P A R A K E E T
I
G                         G
BLUEBIRD          O
    O     O           O
ROBIN     V           S
  W       E A G L E   E
  LARK
```

Tile Tie-Ins (page 8)

```
TOAD      T           C
  L    C  O           H
  L    R  R    L      A
  I    O  T    I      M
  GECKO O  T  Z      E
N  A   D  I  SNAKE  L
E  T   I  E    R      E
W  O           D      O
TURTLE            N
   E
```

Bug Collection (page 9)

This bug appears five times.

Picture-by-Number (page 10)

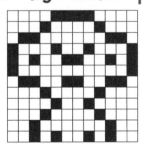

Leapfrog (page 11)

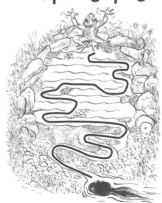

Come Together (page 12)

```
C E N T I P E D E
C O C K R O A C H
E A R T H W O R M
```

Add-a-Letter (page 13)

```
L I O N
T I G E R
B E A R
L L A M A
C A M E L
B I S O N
```

Word Swatter (page 14)

Answers may vary.

```
OWES   WOES
AWES   COWS
ACES   CASE
```

Bee Maze (page 15)

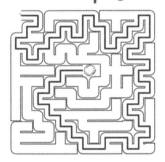

Tile Tie-Ins (page 16)

```
G      SQUIRREL
O      H            L
A      E   HORSE    E
TIGER  T   T        P
       P   T        H
           CHEETAH
ZEBRA  R            N
  E    A   M        T
  A        E
GORILLA
```

ANSWERS

Riddle in the Middle (page 17)

L A B E L
C H A I R
L O B B Y
R H Y M E

S T E A K
D E L A Y
C R E A M
E M P T Y
A C H O O
B R A V E
P U N C H
A C T O R
M E S S Y

Presto, Change-o! (page 18)

1. donkey 2. bat or rat 3. hog 4. moose 5. mole 6. mouse
7. ray 8. boar 9. lion 10. skunk

Crustacean Crossing (page 19)

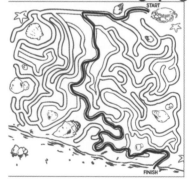

Find the Blocks (page 20)

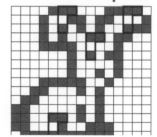

Theme Park (page 21)

F L I E S
G N A T S
M O S Q U I T O E S
B E E T L E S
R O A C H E S
A N T S
W A S P S

Bird Jumbles (page 22)

quail; seagull; eagle; crow; parakeet; ostrich; toucan; penguin

Riddle answer: He quacks up!

Reword Rewind (page 23)

free/reef

A Trail of Threes (page 23)

Pict-o-Matic (pages 24-25)

Come Together (page 26)

A L B A T R O S S

S A P S U C K E R

C H I C K A D E E

Piles of Tiles (page 27)

T I G E R   L I O N
E L E P H A N T
G U I D E   R H I N O
H I P P Y
L A N D R O V E R
H Y E N A

Find the Blocks (page 28)

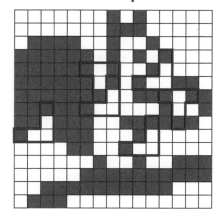

Honey Bear (page 29)

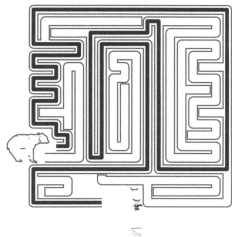

Piles of Tiles (page 30)

Find the Pair (page 31)

B and C are identical. A has a different pattern on the left front wing; D has fewer white lines on its body; E has a different pattern on the right front wing; F has fewer speckles on the two back wings.

Turtle Maze (page 32)

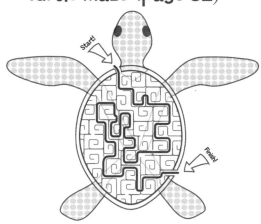

Theme Park (page 33)

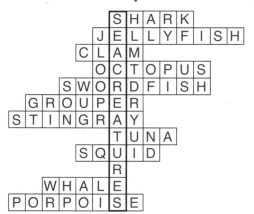

The Ocean (page 34)

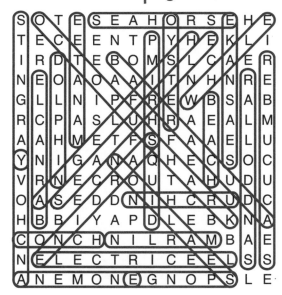

ANSWERS

Picture This (page 35)

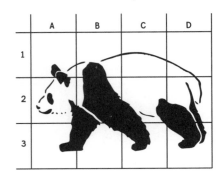

Insect Anagrams (page 36)

mosquito; dragonfly; butterfly; grasshopper; ladybug; caterpillar; beetle; horsefly

Riddle answer: It was a moth ball!

Spiderweb (page 37)

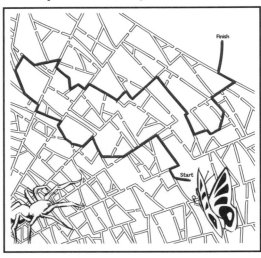

Bird Watching (page 38)

There are 25 birds.

Picture-by-Number (page 39)

Reword Rewind (page 40)

taste/state

Add-a-Letter (page 41)

P E A R
A P P L E
P L U M
L I M E
P E A C H
M A N G O
G R A P E

Pizza Pie (page 42)

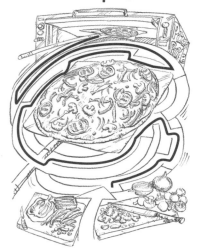

Out on the Farm (page 43)

Pic-doku (page 44)

Add-a-Letter (page 45)

R O S E
I R I S
D A I S Y
L I L A C
P E O N Y
A S T E R
O R C H I D

Road Block Flock (page 46)

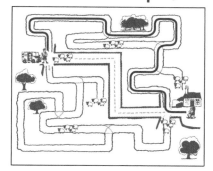

Add-a-Letter (page 47)

B E A N S
P E A S
S P I N A C H
B E E T S
C O R N
T U R N I P S
O N I O N S

Broken Egg #1 (page 48)

96

Tile Tie-Ins (page 49)

```
            P E A C H
    G R A P E     H
M       L         E
A   B L U E B E R R Y
N     A   M       R
G       N   P A P A Y A
O R A N G E       P
    N     A       P
W A T E R M E L O N
          E
```

A Calculated Joke (page 50)

Riddle: What do you call two bananas?
Answer: A pair of slippers!

Trotting Along (page 51)

Picture Picnic (page 52)

Reword Rewind (page 53)

lemon/melon

Crossed Out (page 53)

```
        S
        W
        E
        E
        T
S A L T Y
```

Tile Tie-Ins (page 54)

```
L         C R A B         O
O         L         S     C
B   S C A L L O P   Q     T
S     M     Y       U     O
T       F   S H R I M P   P
E       I       T   D     U
R   M U S S E L             S
        H       R
```

ANSWERS

Number Code: Sounds Like Food (page 55)

1. pair 2. meet 3. stake 4. bred 5. Sunday

Food Anagrams (page 56)

1. hamburger 2. apple pie 3. spaghetti 4. ice cream
5. chicken soup

Until the Cow Comes Home (page 57)

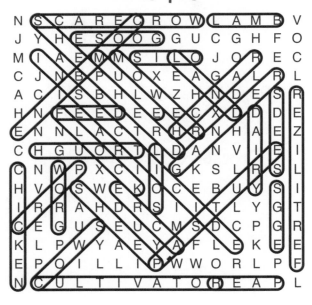

Farming (page 58)

Number Code: Veggies (page 59)

1. peas 2. cabbage 3. carrots 4. lettuce 5. eggplant

Piles of Tiles (page 60)

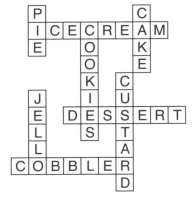

Word Swatter (page 61)

Answers may vary.

SPOIL	SPOOL
LOOTS	POOLS
SPLIT	PILOT
LOOPS	TOILS
TOOLS	STOOP

Straw Vote (page 62)

B. In A, it has a shirt pocket; in C, a haystack is missing; in D, it has a left hand; in E, there is a tree in place of a haystack.

Tile Tie-Ins (page 63)

Round 'em Up! (page 64)

There are 18 cows.

Picture This (page 65)

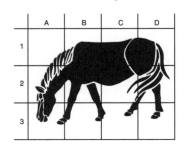

Add-a-Letter (page 66)

B R I C K
C R E A M
E D A M
G O A T
F E T A
C H E D D A R
G O U D A

Pic-doku (page 67)

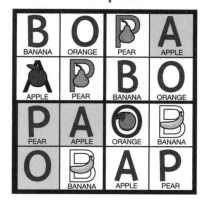

B BANANA	O ORANGE	P PEAR	A APPLE
A APPLE	P PEAR	B BANANA	O ORANGE
P PEAR	A APPLE	O ORANGE	B BANANA
O BANANA	B APPLE	A PEAR	P

Find the Blocks (page 68)

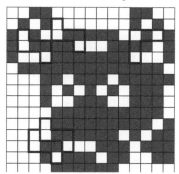

Flower Power (page 69)

A. In B, the bottom flower is missing a petal: in C, the circle is filled in on the sides; in D, the top stem has lost its leaves.

Fruits (page 70)

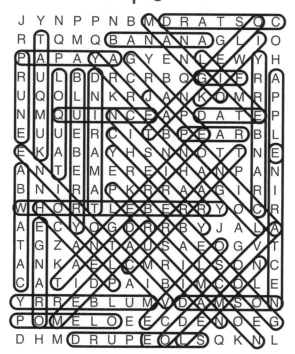

Leaping Labyrinth (page 71)

Sixes and Sevens (page 72)

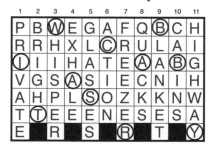

Riddle Answer: It was crabby!

Broken Egg #2 (page 73)

ANSWERS

Word Swatter (page 74)

Answers may vary.

H U N T	S E N T
N E S T	N U T S
H E N S	H U T S
N E T S	S T U N
S H U N	T U N E

Piles of Tiles (page 75)

```
                M
            B   E
    G       L   T
  S A T E L L I T E
    L       A   E
  S T A R   C   O
    A       K   R
    X       H
    Y       O
        C O M E T
            L
            E
```

Lost in Space (page 76)

Sun's Out (page 77)

star

Come Together (page 78)

| V E N E Z U E L A |
| N I C A R A G U A |
| S I N G A P O R E |  DID YOU KNOW?

Theme Park (page 79)

```
        D U N E S
  C A M E L
  O A S I S
    H E A T
  L I Z A R D
```

X Marks the Spot (page 80)

Outer Space (page 81)

```
A S T R O N A U T   P R O
N O O M M N U S R O M E
M E T E O R M T O N E C A
O L S U V W I E N T U R R
S L T U T C L M I L P C T
G R E I R L M A N A R H
D R B E A S L R R Y E
S R A I T A P L M W
O S U M S R Q P D G I K
B I G D I P P E R L Y S
```

Theme Park (page 82)

```
            S U N
A S T E R O I D
        P L U T O
        U R A N U S
        M A R S
    V E N U S
M E R C U R Y
        S A T U R N
      E A R T H
  J U P I T E R
            M O O N
```

Come Together (page 83)

| C H A R L O T T E |
| F O R T W O R T H |
| H O L L Y W O O D |

Leapin' Lava (page 84)

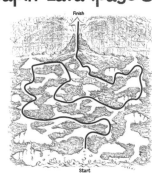

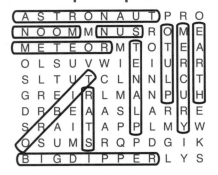

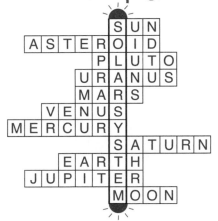

182

ANSWERS

Piles of Tiles (page 85)

```
    M
  T O R O N T O
  O     |   C O L D
  N   Q   N
  T   U   T
  R   E   A
  M A P L E L E A F
  A   B   R
  L   E   I
      C   O
```

European Countries (page 86)

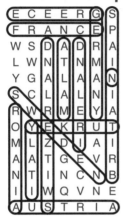

Gold Rush! (page 87)

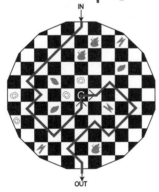

Add-a-Letter (page 88)

```
L I M A
P A R I S
R O M E
T O K Y O
S E O U L
B E R L I N
D U B L I N
```

Secret Spaces (page 89)

Outer Space (pages 90–91)

Crossed Out (page 92)

```
      S
      U
M O O N
```

Crossed Out (page 92)

```
    F
L O C A L
  R
  E
  I
  G
  N
```

Car Chase (page 93)

183

ANSWERS

Tile Tie-Ins (page 94)

```
W  N E W J E R S E Y
A     E
S     V I R G I N I A
H     A        D        R
I  N D I A N A        H  I
N        A     L     O H I O
G              A        N
T E X A S           A
O           K     I O W A
N     U T A H
```

Follow the Trail (page 95)

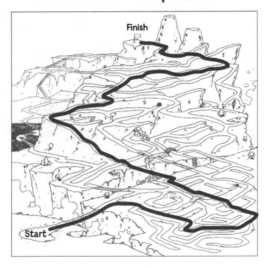

Come Together (page 96)

```
L I T H U A N I A
I N D O N E S I A
S W A Z I L A N D  ← DID YOU KNOW?
```

Picture-by-Number (page 97)

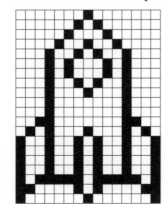

Piles of Tiles (page 98)

```
A        B O S T O N
T        A
L        N           D
A   N E W Y O R K  E
N        R           T
T        A           R
A        N           O
         C           I
      M I A M I      T
         S           T
         C
C H I C A G O
```

Tile Tie-Ins (page 99)

```
M O S C O W     C        T
A           A        A        O
D     B E R L I N     K
DID YOU  → R O M E  S        I        Y
KNOW?      I        A        R        O
D          J        W     O S L O
V I E N N A           I S B O N
         G                    B
            D U B L I N
```

USAnagrams (page 100)

1. California—Sacramento 2. Texas—Austin 3. Florida—Tallahassee 4. New York—Albany 5. Hawaii—Honolulu

Road Map Mystery (page 101)

1. Adam 2. Dana 3. Bill 4. theater

Sarah's Desert (page 102)

Geography Anagrams (page 103)

Ireland, Australia, Germany, Spain, United States

Outer Space (pages 104-105)

1. asteroid belt 2. astronaut 3. comet 4. Earth 5. Jupiter
6. Mars 7. Mercury 8. Milky Way 9. moon 10. Neptune
11. Pluto 12. satellite 13. Saturn 14. solar system
15. Uranus 16. Venus

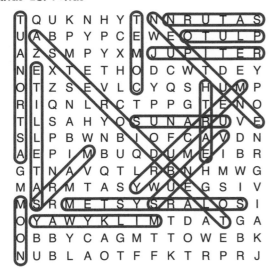

Number Code: States (page 106)

1. Maine 2. Montana 3. Maryland 4. Michigan 5. Missouri

Word Web (page 107)

Word Swatter (page 108)

Answers may vary.

GOAT	ATOM
MATE	TOGA
MEAT	GAME
MOAT	TAME

Home Run! (page 109)

Report Card (page 110)

creative writing: A; digital arts: B; drawing: B; music: A; theater: C. Since his creative writing grade is better than his drawing grade (1), and his drawing grade is better than his theater grade (3), he must have gotten an A in creative writing, a B in drawing, and a C in theater. He got an A in music (4). Since he didn't get an A in digital arts (2), by elimination he got a B in digital arts.

Decoder (page 111)

Riddle answer: Out clubbing!

Number Code: Sports (page 112)

1. hockey 2. soccer 3. squash 4. baseball 5. lacrosse

Gone Fishin' (page 113)

Hoops Commute (page 114)

Emily, North Road, 2nd; Marcia, West Street, 1st; Patti, South Road, 4th; Sara, East Street, 3rd. Patti is the fourth to be picked up (2). Since Marcia is picked up before the friend who lives on North Road who is picked up before Sara (6), Marcia must have been picked up first, the friend on North Road second, and Sara third. Therefore, Marcia lives on West Street (4). Sara isn't picked up on South Road (5), so by elimination, Sara is picked up on East Street, and Patti is picked up on South Road. Also by elimination, Emily is the second picked up.

ANSWERS

Picture This (page 115)

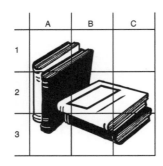

Piles of Tiles (page 116)

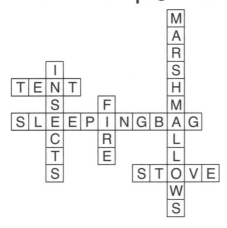

Riddle in the Middle (page 117)

U S **H** E R	D E **C** O Y	M A **J** O R
C L **O** S E	P E **A** C H	C R **U** S T
M O **U** S E	D A **N** C E	C O M **M** A
V I **S** O R	F A **N** C Y	R E **P** A Y
W H **E** E L	S H **O** R T	
W A **S** T E	W I **T** C H	

Snack Attack (page 118)

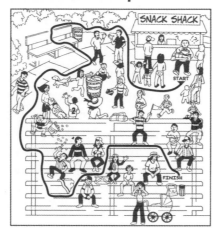

Reword Rewind (page 119)

shop/hops

Word Swatter (page 119)

Answers may vary.

| L A P S | P A L S |
| S L A P | A L P S |

Theme Park (page 120)

BOOTS / BUNNYSLOPE / MOUNTAIN / SNOWSKI / POLES / LIFT / OUTFIT / SNOWBOARD / GLOVES

Add-a-Letter (page 121)

PUCK
RINK
GOAL
STICK
SHOT
GOALIE
CREASE

Jammin'! (page 122)

Decoder (page 123)

Where do we find pirates that don't sail ships, carry swords, or bury treasure?
Answer: Pittsburgh, PA

Where do we find diamondbacks that are red and black, live in the desert, but don't have any rattles?
Answer: Arizona

ANSWERS

Class Schedule (page 124)

camping, period 5; dance, period 2; kickball, period 4; photography, period 1; surfing, period 6; swimming, period 3. In period 2, Olivia has dance class (4). Olivia has surfing in period 6 (2). Since she doesn't have kickball during period 3 (5), but she has camping right after kickball (1), she must have kickball during period 4 and camping during period 5. Since she has swimming later in the day than photography (3), she has photography during period 1 and swimming during period 3.

Theme Park (page 125)

```
    V I O L I N
H O R N
    N   S A X O P H O N E
  F L U T E
    T R O M B O N E
    T U B A
  D R U M
  O B O E
C L A R I N E T
T R U M P E T
C Y M B A L S
```

Tile Tie-Ins (page 126)

```
H Y D R O G E N
            I R O N
  C   Z I N C     I
  O   S     K     T
  P   O X Y G E N R
  P   D     L     O
H E L I U M       G
  R   U           E
      M   C A R B O N
```

Rockin' Road (page 127)

Add-a-Letter (page 128)

G O L F
P O L O
T E N N I S
S O C C E R
R U G B Y
A R C H E R Y

Sketchbook (page 129)

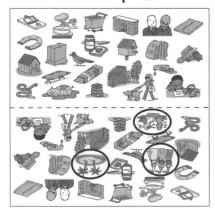

Word Ladder (page 130)

BAIT, bail, boil, coil, cool, cook, HOOK

Word Swatter (page 130)

Answers may vary.

H O R N   H E R O

H O U R   O M E N

M E N U   H O N E

M O R E   N O R M

Tangled Kites (page 131)

ANSWERS

Mathletes Meeting (page 132-133)

Picture This (page 134)

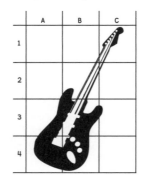

Walking Trail (page 135)

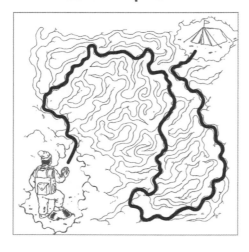

America's Pastime (pages 136-137)

Picture-by-Number (page 138)

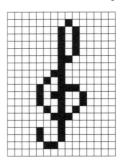

Lunchtime Logic (page 139)

Amy, seat E, brings; Emily, seat A, brings; Holly, seat C, buys; Stacy, seat D, brings; Trudy, seat B, buys; Valerie, seat F, buys. Emily and the two friends in seats D and E bring their lunches (1) so Emily doesn't sit in seats D or E. Valerie sits in seat F (4). Since she doesn't sit in seat D or E, she must buy her lunch. Emily has only one person sitting beside her, and the person in seat C buys her lunch (2), so by elimination Emily is in seat A. Also by elimination, the person in seat B buys her lunch. Holly has only one person sitting by her and she isn't in seat D (3), so she must be in seat C. Trudy sits by Holly (4) so Trudy is in seat B. Since Amy has a person sitting on both sides (3), she must sit in seat E. By elimination, Stacy sits in seat D.

Picture This (page 140)

Track Club (page 141)

Matthew Parker, 5 minutes; Elsie Wakefield, 6 minutes; Tina Smith, 7 minutes; Sam Grant, 8 minutes; Jake West, 9 minutes. Matthew's time was 5 minutes, the person whose last name is Wakefield was 6 minutes, Tina's was 7 minutes, and the person whose last name is West was 9 minutes (1). Since Sam ran one minute faster than Jake (2) but one minute slower than the person whose last name is Smith (4), Sam's time must have been 8 minutes, Jake's was 9 minutes, and the person whose last name is Smith had a time of 7 minutes. Therefore, Elsie had a time of 6 minutes. Since Sam's last name isn't Parker (4), Sam's last name is Grant, and Matthew's last name is Parker.

ANSWERS

Crossed Out (page 142)

```
    S
    T
M O V E
    P
```

Add-a-Letter (page 143)

A U T O
L I M O
B O A T
S E D A N
S H I P
T R A I N

Fit It (page 144)

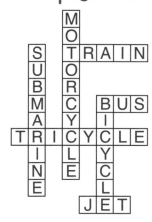

Nice Trike (page 145)

B. In A, there are shadows under the wheels; C is missing front spokes.

Picture This (page 146)

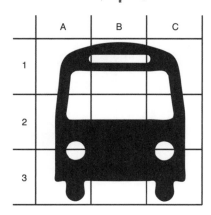

Nuts and Bolts (page 147)

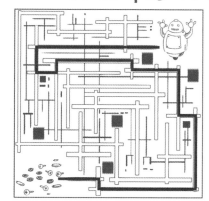

Add-a-Letter (page 148)

F I L E
P L A N E
C H I S E L
M A L L E T
C L A M P
S A N D E R

Decoder (page 149)

Riddle answer: That was uncalled for!

Getting There (pages 150–151)

Treasure Boat (page 152)

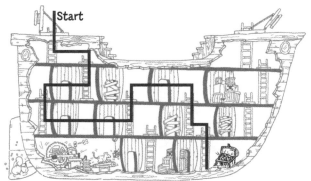

189

ANSWERS

Picture This (page 153)

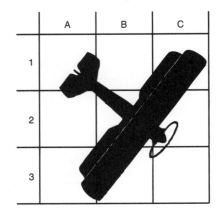

Piles of Tiles (page 154)

```
S E A T B E L T
  I
  S
M     L       C
O V E R H E A D
V             R
I             R
E       T R A Y
              O
C A P T A I N N
```

Reword Rewind (page 155)

fear/fare

Reword Rewind (page 155)

pans/naps/span

Lightbulb (page 156)

All Aboard! (page 157)

Picture This (page 158)

Theme Park (page 159)

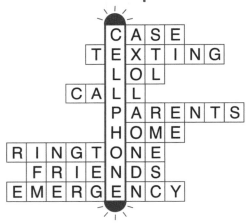

Picture-by-Number (page 160)

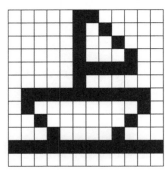

Getting There (page 161)

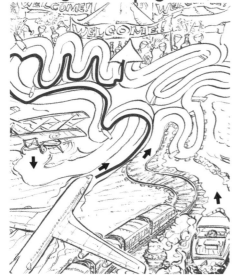

Piles of Tiles (page 162)

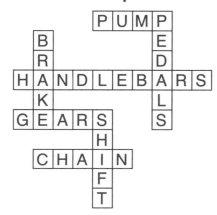

Riddle Scramble (page 163)

HAGRAN H A N G A R

GEEINN E N G I N E

FLUE F U E L

ATELM M E T A L

DRIB B I R D

LIPTO P I L O T

KITETC T I C K E T

EELPOP P E O P L E

A I R P L A N E

Find the Blocks (page 164)

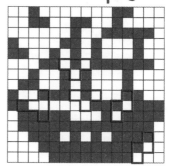

Shoelaces (page 165)

1. C; 2. A; 3. D; 4. B

Word Ladder (page 166)

WALK, talk, tale, sale, same, some, HOME

Word Swatter (page 166)

Answers may vary.

T A B L E S	S T A B L E
T A B L E T	B A T T L E
B E E T L E	L A T E S T

Chain Words (page 167)

Find the Blocks (page 168)

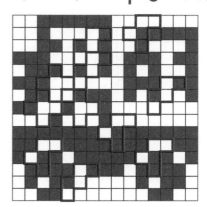

ANSWERS

Picture-by-Number (page 169)

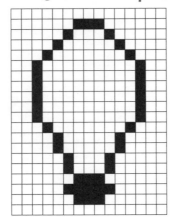

Picture This (page 173)

Road Trip! (page 170)

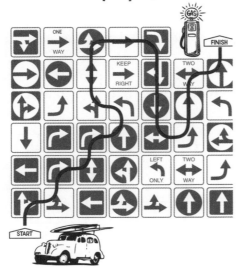

Theme Park (page 174)

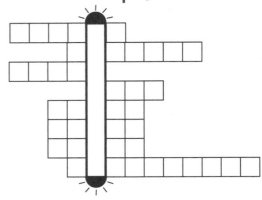

Find the Blocks (page 171)

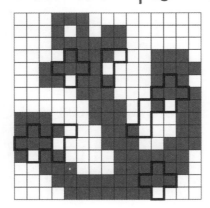

Full Steam Ahead (page 172)

C. In A, there is no shadow under the rear wheels; in B, the cabin has a single window; in D, there is a design on the coal car; in E, the lamp is lit.

192